The Camel Doctor

by M. McCoy Smith, DVM

Contents

Introduction

Dr. William J. Isabell and his wife Anna were lifelong friends, and colleagues in veterinary medicine.

Though we were separated by eight thousand miles and only were together every two years across our lifetime, we were co-laborers together on the continents of America and Africa.

Dr. Bill"s stories and his insatiable love for the camel have brought much delight to me across the years.

In *The Camel Doctor,* I share his stories with you with the hope that they will speak to you as they have to me.

Dr. Mac

DEDICATED TO

ANNA MARIE BOSHEE ISABELL
1922 - 1978

A TRIBUTE

To the children that rode the goats on Sand Mountain

To Miss Bessie that cared for all of our needs in America

To a nearby landmark "Bible Country" with a living, moving background of camels in the desert

To all that went camel riding in the Fringe Country

To Boaz our Good Samaritan near the Sahara Desert

A tribute to Ling and Dr. Mac and Sal and all the others too numerous to mention

To Anna who helped me live all of the true stories and true happenings in America and Africa

To the American Anonymous Foundation that was generous in supplying all of our financial needs

To Anna whom I shall love dearly forever

Prologue

THE STORIES in this book recount some of the amusing, informative, true-to-life happenings across my growing up years in America and my years as a veterinary missionary in Africa. My wife Anna plays a major role in our most interesting life together. Let me relate one little incident which will set the tone for the book and of our relationship together.

It was a very special day — one I had been waiting for with anticipated joy. It's about Anna. My Anna. The Anna I have had for my very own for almost a lifetime. You see, it was her 50th birthday.

Anna and I were very happy in our veterinary practice in the "Fringe Country" of Eastern Africa. Yet, across the years, we maintained a close relationship with our friends and families, in spite of the distance that separated us. As a "camel doctor," I learned that the dependability of this giant animal taught me much and enhanced my relationship with my whole world.

Most people know very little about the camel. Since his natural habitat is located in the lands of the Bible, I was particularly intrigued with them. Many references appear in the Bible to this fascinating beast of burden. I'm sure Abraham knew that the old proverb, "slow but sure," was true of his camels. He sent his eldest, most trusted servant with ten camels, no doubt laden with gifts, to seek a wife for his son Isaac from among his own kindred. Though the trip would take some time, Abraham trusted that when those camels returned, the bride of God's choosing would be riding on one of them.

A few days before Anna's birthday, I went to see my friend Boaz, who owned and operated a large "camel store." No, he didn't buy and sell camels. He was an expert craftsman of jewelry. Camels were his specialty. I knew that with his expertise and creativity, he would make the perfect birthday gift for Anna.

"Boaz," I said, "I want you to make a camel jewelry piece that I can give to Anna for her birthday."

"I can do that," he replied. "I will make whatever you want."

"I want a little camel that can be worn on a necklace," I told him. "I want this camel to be a SHE camel and to be a little smaller than her counterpart, the HE camel," I explained.

"I will write this work order as though Job himself had given it," Boaz remarked. "Job always spoke of his chosen herd of six thousand camels as SHE camels and HE camels."

When Anna's birthday arrived, I went to Boaz' "camel store" to pick up my order. I quickly paid Boaz for his work of art — a lovely SHE camel necklace — and excitedly made my way home to present my gift to Anna. A pleasant smile came over her face and her eyes twinkled as she held the unique gift I had given her. She was very happy that I had chosen this special gift because both of us had come to love the humble camel as our adopted pet.

Nearly a year later, on my 52nd birthday, Anna presented me with a very special present. Wouldn't you know it! It was a beautiful HE camel, a little larger than Anna's SHE camel. Anna explained that I could use it as a watch fob or wear it as a lapel pin.

Across the passing years I have taken great pride in my HE camel jewelry, even as Anna took much pride in her SHE camel necklace.

Chapter One

On the Way to Twenty-one

Goats, Debbie, Giggs, Anna and Me

I HAD KNOWN ANNA all my life, but didn't get very serious about her until our college days. My grandmother lived near her home, so Anna and I were together from the time we were small children.

When I was eight years old, I was the proud owner of three "nannie" goats and one "billy." I rode my billy and the neighborhood children rode the nannies. Debbie, Giggs, Anna and I rode the goats almost every day and always had a wonderful time. The goats didn't like it much but we enjoyed it anyway.

The scruffy creatures soon learned to move very close to the woven wire fence, forcing us to get off their backs. To counter this action, we soon learned to have one of us to lead the goat while the other would ride.

Sometimes my billy goat got free of our grasp and defiantly backed one of us into a corner, threatening to butt with his horns. I quickly learned how to handle his disobedience. I carried a stick of stove wood with me and hit him over the head with it. That cured my billy from showing off.

One day the four of us decided to give the goats a bath. They smelled so bad, and we believed that a bath would certainly help. Since there was no creek or pond nearby, we decided we could use a mud puddle that was formed by an early morning rain.

We threw the little goats down on their sides. They flopped and kicked, bleating for help or mercy with a kind of pitiful cry, like they were begging to be left alone.

When the bathing was over we looked at our little "goats of mud." They certainly were not very clean. In spite of that, each of us ran to get our mothers to see what a fine job we had done on our goat bathing. When our mothers arrived they were horrified. Giggs mother was very angry and blamed the whole situation on me.

"This would not have happened if it were not for Bill," she accused. "He is the ring-leader and should be whipped for leading the others in this escapade. He is the oldest and I know he made the others do this."

"No, let's not punish anyone," Anna's mother, Miss Bessie, said. "Instead, let's have them to draw water from my well and give them some soap. Then they can give the goats a proper bath."

By the time we were through with this tedious chore, our goats were clean and we vowed never to wash the goats again in a mud puddle.

A few months later, our mothers had a conference about the goats. The problem was that each of us smelled like goats everytime we played with the pets. The goats also caused an unpleasant odor, to say the least, throughout the whole neighborhood. They suggested that I get rid of my goats, and offered a dollar bonus for each of the goats I would sell. I found a livestock dealer and sold my goats while my mother was shopping one day. When she returned home she asked when I was going to sell my goats. I told her that I had sold them that day and had the money in my pocket.

"Then why are you riding your billy?" she asked.

"I don't want to sell my billy," I replied. "I need him to ride for myself."

"If you will sell your billy, I will give you an extra, round, shiny, silver dollar, in addition to your dollar bonus," she bargained.

I sold my billy and still have that silver dollar, proudly displayed in a frame. I couldn't understand why our mothers did not like the goats. I didn't think they smelled so bad then. But today, since I am a veterinarian and often have to treat goats in my practice, I approach them with almost the same reluctance as the flushing of a skunk.

Fox Hunting

"Get your heavy coat and see that the lantern is filled with oil." These were the final instructions given by Uncle Noah as we left for our fox hunt. I was fourteen years old and Uncle Noah was taking me on my first fox hunt in the hill country of Alabama.

Fox hunting, as a sport, had originated in England. The fox hunters, mounted on sturdy, fast horses, followed their hounds across countryside ditches, woods, streams and pasture fields. The foxhounds ran in packs and were specially trained for this exciting sport, usually held in England during the daylight hours.

Uncle Noah and I were going fox hunting "American" style. We had our pack of foxhounds, eight in number, and all our needed equipment as we made our way to his special hilltop. It was on the same spot that Uncle Noah built his open log fire and listened to the fox races for the past decade. This year, he had been going on Saturday evening and the weekly race would probably last all night. We decided to build the fire to last for a long time and prepared for the cool night air.

Uncle Noah said, "The race is about the same every Saturday night. All of my dogs are about the same in the pack — except one — 'Old Blue!' He is very special, a real good runner, and is the biggest dog I have ever owned. His wind is extremely good." I could tell "Old Blue" was special to Uncle Noah and I made a point to try to remember this dog.

"I need to tell you about this red fox that always shows up for the race," Uncle Noah went on. "I know he is coming out to run everytime I come up on this mountain, so I just named this special fox 'Big Red.' I've always known this fox is enjoying the *run* as much as the dogs enjoy the *chase*."

Soon the log fire was blazing and it was time to turn the foxhounds loose for the hopeful chase. Every dog in the pack darted out fast, believing that he would catch his fox within the next ten minutes. But not "Old Blue." He just started out slow, kinda warming his running muscles, knowing that the race may be an all night affair. He seemed to decide to hold his wind until later.

It wasn't very long until the pack started barking. They had picked up the scent of a fox. Uncle Noah could identify the barking voice of each of his dogs and told me, "There's Old Tom! And I hear Old Jim, and Old Kate is in on it, too!" Finally, the deep voice of Old Blue could be identified, even by me, a first-time hunter, as very different from the rest of the pack.

Uncle Noah smiled as I saw a flicker of light from the campfire shine across his face. He said, "Well, the big race has started. I can tell Old Blue has found Big Red and now I'll teach you what real fox hunting is all about.'

The race went from hill to hollow, to pasture, to woods and in all directions. The main bark to listen for was Old Blue and Uncle knew that Big Red was leading the pack of foxes as Old Blue was leading the pack of dogs. As the night went on, the dog pack began to sound weaker and weaker. Uncle said that the dogs were just worn out by now and he could tell that they had gone back to the house to rest.

It was nearly daybreak and all the dogs were back at the house, except for Old Blue. Even his bark was weaker and we were sure that Big Red was also weak by this time. They had run all night.

Uncle Noah and I went to the house and as he sat down on the porch, I noticed all the dogs lying in the front yard — asleep. Old Blue was not in yet and as I stood near the fence gate, I saw a big red fox approaching the gate. He was staggering and tired. Directly behind the tired fox was Old Blue, barking with a weakened voice and tired from the all night run.

"Close the gate! Close the gate!" Uncle Noah cried. "The fox is coming into the yard. Close the gate!"

But I did not understand what he was yelling. The big red fox ran into the yard, awaking the rested dogs, and in a few seconds they had caught Big Red and tore him into pieces. Uncle Noah bowed down and cried very loudly as he asked to be forgiven for catching the fox. It seemed that he loved Big Red as much as he loved Old Blue, who had passed out before he reached the gate that eventful morning. Big Red had not been caught and destroyed by his sporting adversary Old

Blue, but by his rested dogs which was very unsports-manlike.

Uncle Noah lost all interest in fox hunting and never went again. He claimed that his rheumatism was acting up and Old Blue was just "give out" and needed the rest. I really believe the real reason Uncle Noah didn't go fox hunting again was that Big Red would never be able to lead the fox run and Old Blue would not have the heart to chase any fox except Big Red.

Hitchhiking
(Adventures While Catching a Ride with Your Thumb)

You can sure meet some strange people while hitchhiking. Take for instance one fellow who stopped for me, a college student, and asked, "What do you have in mind?" Just his look made me think again if I wanted to take this ride.

Of course, None of us students at Auburn University had an automobile in the late 1930s. The accepted mode of travel by male students was hitchhiking.

I vividly remember my first trip as a hitchhiker at a favorite curb near the city limits of my hometown. I had learned the tricks of the trade from my fellow students at the University. You must always look your best including Sunday suit, white shirt, tie, shiny shoes and your ROTC cap in place. You must always act your best in the presence of a possible ride. A smile goes a long way as most drivers pass you by slowly, looking you over, and then decide to stop a hundred feet or so past you.

When you accept a ride, you must also respect the desire of the driver. Sometimes he may want to talk, sometimes he may want you to talk and at other times he desires complete silence with just the hum of the motor breaking the silence. The code of the hitchhiker is universal and rigid, but never seen in print; just observed by everyone using their thumb as a ticket.

In a city about half way to our school, the best place to catch a ride was at a corner near a gasoline station. At the time, the station was engaged in an ambitious advertising scheme which was somewhat common in those days. A flag-pole sitter, atop a forty foot platform, stayed for several days and nights, and attracted thousands of people to the station during his tenure. The motoring public came by almost daily to see if he was still atop the pole. With a loud speaker, he always spoke to the folks in every car that passed. "Hey you!" he would yell. "Stop here and buy some gasoline and please give one or two of these students a ride to the University." It was surprising how quickly we could get a ride with his help. It was almost like a powerful endorsement for a political candidate during election time.

While making my way back to the University one Saturday afternoon, the driver of a big, black General Motors car stopped to give me a ride. The driver was a well dressed man in a dark business suit.

I thanked the man politely for offering me a ride. We talked about football for at least an hour. Suddenly we noticed the car in front of us wobbling from one side of the road to the other. It's driver was very erratic. My new friend pushed a button on the dash of his car and a loud police siren sounded from underneath the hood of his car. The auto in front of us pulled over to the side of the road. We pulled in behind him and my driver got out to question him. He then came back to the car and radioed the local highway patrol to come and take over the arrest duties.

When the drunk driver was in the hands of the highway patrol, I was driven to the front door of the dormitory where I lived.

"I brought you all the way home because you lost time while I was doing my work duties," he explained. Then he gave me a courtesy card with his name printed as the "State Safety Commissioner." My school mates held me in high respect for at least ten days because I had met the highest public safety officer in the state of Alabama.

About 1940, the movie "Gone With the Wind" was scheduled to premier across the state line in Georgia. Two of my classmates and I decided we would hitchhike to Georgia to see the much acclaimed movie. We further decided that we would only take a ride where all three of us could go together. Hundreds of students were standing on the designated corner curb for a ride to Georgia. We called for a "Sound off" and each student shouted his number in order of his arrival. We were numbers 108, 109, and 110. Within thirty minutes we were first, second and third, and soon had our ride to the movie. The show lasted for four and one-half hours and since the sounds of World War II were drawing closer, the movie, even though it was about the Civil War, was very heavy for most of us were of draft age.

It was two o'clock in the morning when the movie was over and we made our way to the standard corner for southwestern hitchhikers. Within ten minutes, the three of us caught a ride home. We noticed the driver was traveling at an excessive rate of speed. About halfway home, he began to get loud and erratic, probably more intoxicated than when he first picked us up. We asked him to let us off at the next crossroad. Even though we hesitated getting out on a dark highway at nearly 3:00 in the morning with traffic almost nonexistent, we felt it was our only safety measure.

It was nearly an hour before we caught another ride. Ten miles up the road, we saw the first car in which we had been riding, turned upside down in the middle of the road. The two occupants were not badly hurt. When we stopped, the driver of the wrecked car recognized us and said, "We lost control as we prepared to turn around and come back for you guys. We felt sorry for leaving you behind." We continued to our dorm and the safety of our school campus — but first thanked our last driver for being generous and driving with such caution and courtesy.

During the summer vacations, I worked at home on the farm raising cotton. One day as I was plowing a five-acre tract across the road from our house with my mule, a friend from the University came to the field. He was dressed in his best suit. He called to me, "You know I am in medical school at the State University, but I need to get home and it is some six hundred miles away. I would like to borrow your ROTC cap and try your way of travel, 'Hitchhiking.'" I went over the rules for hitchhiking: always wear your best suit, clean shirt, tie, shiny shoes and ROTC cap; always act as good as you look and be friendly to everyone. He must have already learned the rules verbally from some of his college buddies. The first time he put out his thumb, he caught a ride all the way to his home.

My last year of college brought some traumatic experiences. I knew that I would be up for the draft and that I had made some mistakes in the priorities of my courses in school. What hurt my pride was that I had not taken the advanced ROTC courses which would have allowed me to enter the Army as a commissioned officer. I had to choose between my summers at home during vacation or being away for extended basic training in the advanced ROTC courses. I decided two years before, when there were no war clouds gathering, that I did not need the advanced training. My calculations were wrong! My future was clouded! My plans were uncertain!

During spring break, I dressed according to all the rules of hitchhiking, put on my old ROTC cap and put out my thumb, hoping to catch a ride. I didn't know where or why I was going. I just wanted to get away to some motel where I could sit and think. I headed east for the coast.

I do not remember any of the rides I caught, or any of the places I spent the night, with the exception of one. One night as I stopped at a motel, I was told that no rooms were available. I asked the clerk if there was any other motel close by where I wouldn't have to walk very far.

"If you're walking and have no other way to get to another motel, I would suggest that you try Mrs. Ross' boarding house, one block up the street," he offered.

Mrs. Ross greeted me and said, "You are dressed clean with a good looking suit and tie. I like to keep people that dress like somebody." I stayed at her boarding house, in a very clean room, which rented for two dollars per night.

"I don't have anyone to eat supper with me and would like to have you join me," Mrs. Ross told me when I checked in. I accepted as quickly as I had accepted my hitchhike rides all day. We ate a very good fried chicken supper and Mrs. Ross assured me that in this case, the meal goes with the room charge.

After dinner, Mrs. Ross sensed my problem of uncertainty. "Young man, you are traveling somewhere because you are disturbed about something," she began. "Don't worry. You are not alone. Many younger, as well as older people are disturbed because of these uncertain days. Just be careful while looking for the answer.

"I know about your university because of your ROTC cap and I know that it is many miles away. If you are so far away, and traveling all alone, it must be that you are trying to find yourself." Mrs. Ross hesitated for a moment and then looking me in the eyes she asked, "Does anyone know you are traveling this path alone?"

"I have told no one and now, you, a stranger, are my only confidant," I confessed.

"You don't have to tell anyone. Just be careful as you travel," she warned. I left the next morning after paying Mrs. Ross the two dollars I owed her.

"I'll even take your mother's place in relation to this trip," she said. "Please think of me as you would of your mother and remember, I'll be mentioning you in constant prayer as you find yourself." I thanked her for her concern and we waved a parting "goodbye."

I found myself at the Atlantic Ocean — as far east as I could go! I had never seen the ocean before. The tide's big billows looked one hundred feet high to me. The white rolling waves came crushing in on the shore one after the other. The spray from the waves caused a heavy mist and made visibility nearly impossible. I found myself trying to look around every wave. It was impossible to see over the rolling tide. After about an hour of this unexplained, impossible way to understand this mystery of the ocean, I felt an easy and calm feeling inside.

I knew that my hitchhiking trip had been resolved, that my future would work out for the best. I understood that I must do my best, whatever the future held, in the Army or any other way of life, and live each day the best I could.

I also realized that it was only God who could control such a vast ocean and only He could control one small person like me. I believe Mrs. Ross was faithful in my behalf. My exploring, hitchhiking mission had accomplished what I needed and I returned to my University campus.

In one of my classes I remember one great philosopher who stood out above the rest. Socrates was a Greek philosopher who lived after 500 B.C. He believed that truth was to "Know thyself." He taught that we should be open to all people, and to use high standards in our code of thinking. The ruling powers of his day however, believed that we should "Hide ourselves." Because of his dissenting beliefs, he was put to death in 399 B.C.

I wish Socrates had been a fellow "hitchhiker" or the owner of a car that gave me a ride. Many times, the driver of an automobile would give a ride to a hitchhiker as a ploy to talk to us and/or to hear us talk.

One Sunday afternoon, I stood at our corner for a ride to the University campus some sixty miles away. A man and his wife picked me up and during the next hour we talked about many moral thoughts concerning the Ten Commandments in the Bible. He was not pushy or domineering. He just wanted to know my thoughts about some moral issues. They took me to the front door of my dorm and I thanked them properly before waving goodbye.

Six months later, I was on the same corner again, and the same man and woman picked me up again. We never exchanged names but did continue our talk from six months previous.

A few months later, as I stood on the same corner at about 10:30 on a Sunday morning, I noticed a big beautiful church across the street. I thought for a while, and since I had on my best suit and was presentable, I decided to attend their morning worship service which was about to begin.

"Today my sermon is on the subject 'Know Thyself,' which is condensed from a talk I had with a hitchhiker as we rode to nearby Auburn University," the minister began. Immediately, I recognized the man as the one who had picked me up across the street on two previous occasions and took me to my dorm.

When leaving the sanctuary, I shook hands with him. He was so surprised to see me and announced to those standing around him, "This is the hitchhiker that helped me write my sermon today and I don't even know his name!" We finally exchanged names and his wife invited me to have Sunday dinner with them. They drove me back to the University and I learned that it was a regular Sunday practice, one which they had been doing for several years. Yet I had passed their way only three times.

Most of the young men at the University went home for summer vacation by hitchhiking. The young ladies took the bus. In all my four years at the University, and many thousands of miles as a hitchhiker, I never saw a girl hitchhiking. We used to laugh when the girls would wave from the bus as they passed us standing on the corner waiting for a ride. Then, after we caught a ride, we would wave to them as we passed their slow, poky bus.

I remember the last trip I ever made, using my thumb as my ticket. As I finished school, I knew that a stint in the military for World War II awaited me. I hitched a ride for the 250 mile trip home. Anna took the bus. The first ride I got took me the complete distance and I had to wait at the bus station for Anna to arrive, which was to be about one hour later.

I had noticed that the sky looked a little disturbing and it was quite windy on the trip home. But there were no difficulties. After waiting for several hours in the bus depot, the weather report announced that wind, rain, and a tornado had caused many vehicles to be blown and washed off the road in the area where Anna was traveling. Further news from the bus terminal indicated that Anna's bus had been involved. We were told repeatedly to just wait a little longer. All the while I prayed for a pure heart and the faith to believe that Anna would arrive safely.

After six hours of delay, just before daybreak, a big bus, outlined by its brightly burning lights, arrived. The prettiest girl I had ever seen jumped from the bus and ran to me, falling into my arms. Then a bus porter tapped Anna on the shoulder and said, "Ma'am, this must be your baggage. It is the last that's on the bus. All the other folks are gone."

Anna and I have had each other ever since — three decades later. That morning I knew my hitchhiking days were over. Though I had arrived before her, when she came, my heart was prepared to receive her to myself for our lifetime!

Chapter Two

Desert Veterinarian

Fringe Country

I VIVIDLY REMEMBER the first day I stood, holding my Boston bag containing a stethoscope and a hypodermic syringe, on the land known as the "Fringe Country" of Ethiopia, bordering the desert. I was ready to investigate and treat the needs of the various animals of this foreign community.

Even though I felt quite alone in this strange country, my task was before me. I had the assurance of at least three friends to help me, even though two of these friends were nearly 8,000 miles away in America.

My first friend was Anna Marie Boshee, my girlfriend who I had known all my life. She was raised on a farm in Alabama as was I. Her training at the university was in Home Economics.

My second dear friend was Dr. Mac, whose training was also in veterinary medicine. He received his degree from my alma mater the same year I came to the Fringe country. His plans, however, were to set up a practice in Northern Tennessee.

My third friend and colleague, Sal Salasie, a native of the Fringe country of Ethiopia. Sal studied agriculture at the university during my last four years as a student there. After completing his studies, he had returned to Ethiopia with plans to become an Agriculture Agent.

My reasons for coming to Ethiopia were many, but the most outstanding was Sal's invitation. "Come home with me and I shall help you with your Veterinary practice." During the last year of our studies at the university, we had had several long talks about his "Fringe country." I was especially interested since my parents were Christian missionaries in Africa. Though I was born in the United States, my parents had taken me to this continent for several years when I was a small boy.

Sal and I had talked for hours as he explained, between my questions, the customs, topography, lifestyles and animals of his native country. One day, straight out of the blue, he asked, "How would you like to go with me to see the Fringe country of Ethiopia?" I thought of several reasons why I should not waste my time going with him, but the most valid one was that it would be too many miles and too long a time away from Anna.

I had to talk with Anna! One clear, moonlit evening, Anna and I were standing in front of the old university library building, which was the most public-private dating place on campus.

"Anna," I began. "As you know, Sal and I are graduating this spring. He has asked me to go home with him to the Fringe country to spend a year or so before settling down to my real practice."

"Bill, you know that you will waste a lot of time chasing around the world doing nothing for a few years," Anna quickly replied. "Why don't you just find a small, county-seat town somewhere around here? You could have a great practice right here at home."

Anna went on to remind me that my American citizenship and birth were more valid reasons to stay in this country than to go to Africa, just because my parents had been missionaries to Africa during part of my growing up years.

Sal and I had become close friends during my last four years at the university. I'm sure that our closeness was strengthened because I was the only person on campus who had ever spent any time in his country.

For several days Anna I continued to discuss the possibilities of my going to Ethiopia. I could tell that it was a very difficult decision for Anna, but one day she told me, "Bill, I will miss you very much, but maybe you should go home with Sal for a year or two." I hugged her closely while tears of joy flooded my eyes. I hurried to tell Sal that I would be going home with him. He was happy when he heard the good news. A big smile flashed across his face and he embraced me.

This new country was very strange and difficult to understand. Ethiopia is an empire located in Northeastern Africa. As one of the world's oldest Christian countries, it lies on the northeastern coast of the Red Sea. Somaliland and French Somalis sprawl to the east, Kenya to the south, and Sudan to the west.

Most of Ethiopia lies on two great plateaus that stand above the surrounding desert lowlands. Great cliffs in wall-like appearance stand around the plateaus, with ravines and canyons cutting many sections. The plateaus have fertile soil and mild climate with temperature ranges of 34° to 90° Fahrenheit. The farming area between the marginal desert and marginal fertile plateaus has its own definition, "Fringe country." Four million Ethiopians live in this area and maintain the most independent lifestyle in the entire country.

I recall musing, *This is where Sal lives and where I intend to live as a missionary veterinarian for his people, at least for one or two years!*

Wear this Suit and Drive this Jeep

I lived in a small house made of white mud walls and a sheet metal roof. The first several weeks were spent cleaning and fixing up the place and getting my personal things together. After all, this was going to be home for awhile. The house had been built for Christian missionaries some twenty years prior to my living there. It was located on the road near Sal's farm. The missionaries stayed for ten years and then went back to the United States.

Sal's farm was operated like most tenant farms in the United States, although the tenants usually live their entire

25

lives on the same farm. They own their own cows, goats, sheep and chickens, and raised all their millet for bread.

Before going to the Fringe country, Sal reminded me that I would probably not have any trouble with the language since the major language taught was English. Sal completely forgot to tell me, however, that ninety percent of the people never attend school, and most of them spoke many different languages and dialects.

An old, one-room school house stood one hundred yards from my house. It was abandoned, except that some of the farmers stored their millet seed in it. I planned to ask Sal if I could use the old building for a veterinary clinic.

The next day was such a bright day. I felt like I could see twenty miles. In the distance, I saw that someone was coming down the road in a cloud of dust. I said to myself, "It looks like Sal, but if it is, he is driving a shiny, new Jeep and it sounds like it is purring on all four cylinders."

Sal came to the door and said, "Doctor Bill, come outside a moment," as he handed me the keys to the new Jeep.

"Are you going to the barter store for the mail?" I asked. "Do you want me to drive your new Jeep?"

"No," he replied. "I want you to drive *your* new Jeep!"

"My new Jeep," I exclaimed! I felt ten feet tall as I slid behind the wheel. I imagined I had the largest practice in the whole world, yet I had never made the first visit to see a sick cow, or sheep, or goat, or camel.

The post office was located in the barter store. Many things were traded for items needed. One man, who looked like a Hebrew, brought his millet to trade for cotton cloth. He wanted some cloth to make pants and shirts for the men, and other white material to make dresses for the women.

I watched the barterer as he commanded his camel to kneel outside the store. On the camel's back was a large wooden platform loaded with about four hundred pounds of millet. When the millet seed sacks were all unloaded, and at the proper command, the camel stood up straight on his long skinny legs.

Back inside the barter store, I asked for my mail. There were two letters from Anna. Aside from some trivial news, she repeatedly asked, "When are you coming home?" *Coming home, I thought, I've only been away twelve days!*

Worming Cows — Is This the Vet?

The middle of July in the Fringe country is the time of year when the grass is the most lush. The cows busy themselves with eating, heads to the ground, taking in grass as fast as they can bite it off. Even the goats and sheep grab the grass as fast as they can as if it were going to evaporate before they finish eating.

One morning Sal came by and said, "I want you to make a vet call with me."

Oh boy, I thought. *What animal will I see? Do I have the proper drugs?*

Sal could see that I was excited and led me toward the Jeep. He said that I should do the driving and diagnose the animals we would see. His job would be to hold the animals for me.

Sal directed me down a road that led through a desert rise, then suddenly into the lowland area. We bumped along the dirt road. To the east rose the cliffs, sharp lines projecting upward from the lush green carpet of grass of the lowlands.

"It is only like this about three months out of the year," Sal said. "So enjoy it!"

After traveling three miles, we came to a farm where I saw a great number of cattle.

As we arrived at the house, Sal introduced me to Mr. Roas, who began telling me about his cows.

"My cows are very thin, as you can see," he said. "Every year about this time, they begin to lose weight and many of them die, even though this is the best pasture grass I have."

As I looked over his herd, my heart sank. His cattle were gaunt and emaciated. They looked hungry and weak. Their skin appeared to be as dry as tanned leather.

I asked Mr. Roas if the cows and calves usually had such loose bowels as they now had.

"What kind of treatment has been tried before?" I asked.

"Nothing has ever been used," he replied.

I got the idea that there had been no treatment of any kind for the cattle in the Fringe country. Yet, I wanted my first diagnosis to be accurate and to be able to give specific, positive results. At that point I prayed, "Lord, I need help and I need it now!"

"Catch that cow standing there," I told Sal and Mr. Roas. To my surprise, the cow did not have to be caught. She just stood there while I got a sample of fecal material. I collected fecal samples from six of the animals.

"Let's go," I said to Sal.

"What's wrong with the cows?" Mr. Roas and Sal asked in unison.

"I believe I can give you a correct diagnosis tomorrow," I answered.

We stopped by the barter store to see if I had any mail or shipment of drugs. A large box of drugs had arrived. Fortunately, it also contained my microscope. When we got back to the house, I fixed the scope stage and lamp and was ready to begin checking the fecal samples.

When I peered through the microscope, I could hardly believe my eyes. All of the samples showed extreme infestation of parasites. Plain and simple, the cows were infested with worms. The worms were consuming all the nutrients in the food the cows ingested. The cows were dying from malnutrition, in spite of the lush grass they had to eat.

The next day, the cattle were wormed and Mr. Roas did not lose any more cows or calves.

Across the next several months, Sal took me from farm to farm throughout the lowland country and on most of them I made the same diagnosis — parasites. Gratefully many cattle were saved through this worming process. God had heard my plea for help and had given it, right on time!

And then there is Ling, a young man who had become very interested in veterinary medicine. One morning in the old school building clinic, I explained the use of the microscope to Ling. "The scope has three powers," I said.

"I know," he replied. "I have already read about the scope in this little book while you were out on a call. But I didn't bother any of your equipment. I was afraid I might break something," he explained.

We didn't talk about it much more at the time, but in short order, Ling learned to use the microscope. He became very accurate with it and used it very well.

One morning, during the first few weeks in the Fringe country, there was a weak knock at the door. When I opened it, a small native Ethiopian man stood timidly looking in my eyes.

"Good morning, Mr. Cow Doctor," he said smiling.

"Good morning to you," I replied. "Would you like to step inside?"

"No, I will be all right here. But I need to ask you about something," he responded.

"That's fine. Go ahead."

"I have been hearing about the cows that have been getting sick and dying like they do every year," the little man explained. "I just want to know how many cows do I have to have sick before you can come and help me?"

"Never less than one," I said jokingly.

"Can I ride with you in the Jeep to see my cow?" he asked.

"Oh yes, we'll go right now," I told him.

Sure enough, I diagnosed his cow (he only had one) had intestinal parasites. I treated his cow and she recovered quickly. Within two months she had good body flesh and had become healthy.

How this little man appreciated what I had done for him (or for his cow)! I had gained a real friend!

A Real Live Camel

One morning I arose early to greet a very hot day. The air was stifling, bringing in heat from the desert many miles away. Though the sun was barely up, the temperature was already 90 +°. Everything around was barely moving.

Ling had been helping me in the clinic since my practice picked up. I would probably need him more regularly. He and his family had been tenant farmers on Sal's family farm for many years.

Ling had cleaned all of my instruments and placed them neatly into the compartments of my veterinary satchel. He asked if it would be all right to turn the Jeep around and park it beside the small practice building, ready to go when needed to treat a sick animal. No sooner than I had said yes, I noticed something moving very slowly coming up the road in the direction of the clinic. The desert haze distorted my identity, but sure enough, it was a real live camel.

I had seen a few camels around the countryside, but as yet, none seemed to need my help. At this point, I almost went into a frenzy! I have never treated a camel before and here comes one now!

"What will I do if its owner wants me to treat him?" I said to myself. "I have never been near to a camel. How shall I approach this animal? How shall I stand tall enough to examine this huge animal, with legs twice as long as those of a horse? Or will it kneel?" While these thoughts were running through my mind, the Hebrew man leading the camel stopped squarely before my door.

"Good morning," I greeted. "That's a good looking camel you have."

"Thank you, Mister Camel Doctor," he replied.

I was both fascinated with his camel and frightened by what he said. He called me a camel doctor, and I had never been near a camel before. This was the first time I had ever seen a camel this close and I certainly never doctored one.

I nervously tried to talk my way into getting a diagnosis of the camel's sickness from its owner. The little man didn't say a word. He let me ramble on, trying to find a clue to the camel's pain or mysterious actions.

Oh, Lord, I need some help here, I prayed silently.

"What seems to be wrong with this nice camel?" I asked.

"Nothing is wrong with my camel today," he replied. "I just wanted to tell you my name, and where I live so that you will know to come see my camel when I need you at the birth of her calf."

He politely told me his name and directions to where he lived and left with a quiet, "Goodbye, Mister Camel Doctor."

Suddenly I felt weak. I knew that delivering a calf from a cow is often difficult, and that delivering a colt from a mare is much more difficult than a cow, because of its long legs and neck. But, to deliver a camel with legs and neck twice as long as a colt's would undoubtedly be extremely difficult.

I knew that I had to start to "camel school" right away. But where? I immediately wrote to the Veterinary school from which I had graduated. Their reply stated that they had no scientific information or literature, or any practical information about camels. They further stated that if I should get any practical information about the camel, I would probably be the only camel veterinary specialist in the world. I didn't care about being a specialist right now. All I wanted to know was how to deliver a camel's calf.

My knowledge about the camel was limited. The camel is one of the most ugly of all animals. It also can be among the most mean. Yet, at the same time, it can be beautiful in its own way and even gentle. The camel is the greatest burden-bearer of all animals. The Bible tells us that camels were given as a gift to Abraham, and that Job had six thousand camels.

My initial examination of the camel told me that it is a shaggy, awkward, stiff-legged, goose-necked, hump-backed beast. It has a split upper lip, pop eyes, loosely hung jaws, a stupid, sad expression, and a face that is too small for its body. It also has fits of anger interrupted by sullen and sad expressions. The camel is so inconsistent that it cannot be fully trusted, even by its owner, nor does it have very many friends, even among other camels.

Yet, here she was. The one animal that was most necessary for the survival of desert peoples. *Guess I had better become acquainted with them, and fast,* I thought.

The Cow Doctor Learned Quickly

I had been talking to Sal about what he was proposing to do to improve our community agriculturally. The soil seemed to be lacking in fertility and it definitely needed more water.

Sal said that many of the nutrients necessary for growing crops showed up very low when he sampled the soil. He was determined, however, to improve conditions. He had made progress on many farms by upgrading the quality of dairy herds through selective breeding.

One morning a man burst into the clinic, out of breath, and quickly greeted me with "Good morning, Mister Cow Doctor!"

I had quickly learned when I am greeted with "Mister Cow Doctor" or "Mister Goat Doctor," I know what animal requires my help.

"My name is Jacob and we don't have much time to go where I live, because my cow is nearly dead," he said in one quick breath.

We climbed into the Jeep and sped to his house. When we arrived, a good-looking milk cow was lying stretched out on the ground. She was shivering and shaking. Her sides were extended and she panted with shortness of breath.

Jacob told me that she was all right earlier in the day when he milked her and that she had given a lot of milk.

I knew that this was to be my first "milk fever cow" in the Fringe country. I prayed, *Dear Lord! You and I both know this is a milk fever case. But please, dear Lord, help me to a perfect job of treating her.*

The first thing I did was to clean the area around the jugular vein with alcohol. Then I got 500 cc's of calcium gluconate, intravenous tubing and a large needle, coupled the tubing to hold the solution in the air for gravity flow, and slowly injected the fluid into the vein. Calcium gluconate must be injected slowly to avoid shock.

The cow started to shake uncontrollably, which was normal as the fluid began circulating to her muscles. In thirty minutes she was able to stand up and "mooed" to her calf which had been standing nearby during the procedure to come to her. When it came to her side, she began to affectionately lick it.

"Mister Cow Doctor," Jacob reminded me. "You came to see me one time when my cows were infected with worms. Within a few weeks my cows got well and became real fat. This cow was sicker than the others and you got her well and perfect, real quick. You sure have learned a lot since the last time you were here!"

Jacob told me to wait in the Jeep because he had something he wanted to give me. He returned shortly, carrying a large bag of millet.

"I want to thank you, Mister Cow Doctor," he said as he handed me the bag of millet.

"No! No!" I replied. "You keep the millet. You and your family may need it.

The sad expression in Jacob's eyes told me he was about to cry because of my rejection of his payment. So I reached out my hands to accept his gift.

"I sure do thank you for this, and I'll remember you each time I eat my wonderful millet bread," I told him.

On the way back to the clinic Sal informed me that his people do not give anything to anyone, unless they mean for the person to take it. They consider it an insult to refuse a gift from another. Yes, I had learned a lot!

Eleven Months in Waiting

Ling came to work driving his father's Jeep. He entered the clinic with a cardboard box. When I asked him the contents of the odd shaped container, Ling said, "You may sit and rest while I open it." It contained an artistic picture of two camels made by someone skilled in marquetry, which is an inlay of contrasting woods. Ling said in a reserved voice, "I carved and assembled the inlays myself as an early marriage gift to you and Miss Anna."

I said, "Anna and I thank you, especially since it portrays two one-humped camels with riders aboard. This is a good time to ask you about your ancestry."

Ling answered, "My father's name is Son Ling Sr. and my mother's name is Mi Ling and my name is Son Ling Jr. We are medium height and light brown complexion. One would know that we are not native Ethiopians. My father and mother are Chinese and lived in Thailand. My father had a small wholesale shipping business to Ethiopia of teak wood and lac.

"You might want to know, lac is a sticky substance from certain insects found only in Thailand, and used in manufacturing of shellac and sealing wax. These products have been essential to making marquetry furniture and pictures for thousands of years."

Ling continued, "My father wanted to get into the furniture making business. When I was two years old we moved from Thailand to the Fringe country of Ethiopia. My father and Sal's father created a partnership of marquetry furniture manufacturing."

Our conversation came to a halt as we noticed someone driving their Jeep faster than usual and holding their basket hat in place as they abruptly stopped in our driveway.

"Good morning, Mister Camel Doctor," he said. I recognized that it was Boaz, who had brought his camel to my clinic and introduced himself to me nearly eleven months before. The gestation period surely had not been completed. Or had it?

"My camel is trying to birth her calf," Boaz exclaimed.

I looked to see if all my instruments and drugs were in place. Of course, Ling had taken care of these.

"You'd better come along with us," I told Ling. "I have been planning to go on this call for nearly eleven months and I can use all the help I can get." I told Ling to drive. I sat next to him in the front and Boaz rode with us in the rear.

When we arrived, the big camel was standing and her water bag had already broken. The membranes were protruding halfway to the hocks. I got my hands washed and lubricated while wondering how I was going to get this job done. The camel was almost twice as tall as I was. I asked Boaz to try to get his camel to lie down. With the proper command, the big camel slowly laid down on the ground, not like she usually kneels for cargo loading, but all the way down. I examined the vulva and two front feet and the nose of the calf were protruding in the normal calving position. I gave the proper hormone injection and in less than ten minutes the calf was born. In fifteen minutes it was standing, and in thirty minutes it was nursing its mother.

Now I could go home and write my friend, Dr. Mac in the U.S., that I had delivered a camel's calf. I'll also ask him how long it has been since he has done this for a camel?

Ling drove me back to the clinic. I don't think either of us said a single word. At any rate, today, I had become Mister Camel Doctor.

Early the next morning, Boaz came to the clinic to tell me the camel and her calf were doing fine. Boaz said, "The reason I had you come when my camel gave birth was last year the calf was stillborn."

I said, "Boaz, I must be honest with you. I never attended a camel while birthing her young before. I just examined her physically to see that everything was in order and no obstruction to delivery, then I timed her labor rhythm of contractions as though she were a cow. And I gave her the hormone injection according to her weight and everything turned out very well."

Boaz said, "I really thank you."

The conversation lagged, but I could tell Boaz had something else on his mind. Finally, it all came out.

Boaz said, "Dr. Bill, will you let me look at the camel marquetry picture Ling gave you yesterday?"

I said, "Let's go over to the house and see it."

Boaz related, "Marquetry originated in this country of Ethiopia. The first known article of this furniture was a gift from Ethiopia to Ramsus II, King of Egypt in 1200 B.C. I believe this art form enhances the friendship of our countries."

Boaz continued, "Ling worked two years on your camel marquetry picture and did an excellent job."

I said, "Should I pay him for the picture?"

Boaz said, "No, as a Chinese, he does things for 'Honorable Father' and 'Loving Mother,' and you are 'Honorable Veterinarian.' He respects you but don't be surprised if he asks you to help him to go to college and get a DVM degree someday, but don't push it."

I said, "I wish he would and be my colleague, but I won't push. I'll just let him make the decision."

Boaz continued, "Dr. Bill, this is confession day. An old unwritten Hebrew law says each Hebrew must find a friend that is not of our own nationality and make ourselves a helper on any need this friend may have in their lifetime. My wife Rebekah and I have decided we will be your helpers as though we were brothers."

I said, "Boaz, I thank you very much."

Boaz left for home in his Jeep. I climbed into my Jeep to make a trip to see a sick milk goat. As I traveled along the road, Boaz' words rang in my ears, "I'll be your friend and your brother forever."

Chapter Three

Proposal to Marriage

Bill Proposed — Anna and Tommy Respond

I HAD NOTHING to do that night, except to think about Anna, and that thought was not so pleasant because she was eight thousand miles away.

My Anna comes from a family of nine children. I remember her telling me about her younger brother Tommy, who was quite a live wire when a child and easily excited about everything. One night when a boyfriend was late for a date and because he had not called to inform her, Anna decided to turn the lights down low to make him think he was too late for the scheduled date.

Tommy was already in bed and was apparently having a bad dream. When he rang the doorbell, Tommy was startled awake, thinking it was a burglar. He jumped out of bed and quickly crawled under the bed to hide.

This incident came to mind as I wrote Anna that evening.

Dear Anna,

This eight thousand miles between us at this moment is going to be reduced to zero within a few months. I have a few things to tell you in the meantime.

First, tell Tommy to stay out from under the bed, and to keep all your other boyfriends away for me. Also, tell him to keep the one with the funny looking vest away from you for sure. If there are any other young men, before or after these, they are to quit seeing you now!

As for you, Anna, when I come home, we are to get married ten days after I arrive home. Consider this letter as your "ten day notice!"

All my love,

Bill

Ten days after I sent Anna this letter of proposal, or declaration of command, or whatever it may be called, I received my first telegram in the Fringe country. It was sent to: Dr. William J. Isabell, Post Office, Barter Store I, Ethiopia, Africa.

The telegram held a simple reply:

I ACCEPT MY ASSIGNMENT - TOMMY BOSHEE
I ACCEPT MY ASSIGNMENT - ANNA MARIE BOSHEE
LOVE, ANNA

As I read the response, a deep sense of peace and gratitude came over me. I knew that I had been accepted by Anna and her family.

Big Wheel in Africa

One day, shortly after I had received the encouraging news from Anna and Tommy, I hoped I would not have any animals to treat. All I wanted to do was to sit and day dream about Anna. I thought, *I guess she has been my real, true girl for many years, but soon she will be my wife. She will be mine for all time, wherever we may be, in the U.S., or Africa, or any other place. Whatever her heart desires, my heart will desire as well.*

What strange words I had written to her. To say the least, the circumstances which had brought me to the Fringe country were unusual. Yet, I knew that I was where I was supposed to be. And I knew that she was the only one for me and her telegram had confirmed that I was the only one for her.

While I was taking my basic courses in Agriculture at the University, my parents were missionaries in South Africa. World War II had just begun, and as an American citizen of proper age, I was subject to the draft. The spring semester was nearly over and soon I would be out of school for the summer.

The war was the number one subject of discussion on campus. The possibility of being included in the draft was the prime topic for the young men. In countries like where my parents were, most people lived in rural areas, so little news of war or politics ever reached them.

One day, before the end of the semester, as I entered the main Agricultural building, I noticed a large poster on the bulletin board. There he was — Uncle Sam — with his finger pointed right at me and his eyes riveted on mine. The sign read:

YOU MAY QUALIFY FOR A.S.T.P.
(Army Specialized Training Program)

If you are a male student, eighteen years of age or older, and have the proper pre-Veterinary courses, you may become a Bonafide-Matriculant in the School of Veterinary Medicine, leading to a degree of Doctor of Veterinary Medicine.

If you have completed two years of basic Agriculture courses, you may qualify.

I read the notice over three times to make sure it was really so. With my heart pounding at the possibilities it offered, I rushed out of the building and raced to Mac's room as fast as I could.

I burst into his room and breathlessly stammered, "Uncle Sam needs you. I mean, Uncle Sam needs us."

Startled, Mac looked up and said, "Who needs Who? For what?"

39

I then explained the notice I had read. Then Mac became more excited than I was. After all, both of us could qualify because we had two years of Agriculture and our grades were good. It was just a matter of making an appointment with the recruiting officer and the rest would be routine.

We were accepted into the Veterinary school and both took the A-ASTP. We added the first A because it became an Accelerated Army Specialized Training Program.

The program was so accelerated that we had to finish the normal four-year program in two years and nine months. We attended school seven days a week, but were allowed two hours off to attend church if we desired. Most of the time we attended church but fully expected that there would be an Army "Roll Call" there as well. Our class had fifty-eight members, which was not very big according to the way the Army counts numbers.

I had always liked Mac. We were the closes of friends. I suspect it was because we were so much alike. Both of us had always had to struggle with our shyness. The rigorous demands of the A-ASTP and its discipline certainly helped us both in this respect.

Answering "roll call" in a regular classroom was hard for me, but it wasn't so bad in the Army program. With the platoon at attention in a straight line, the officer would call: Adams, Here!; Anderson, Here!; Bishop, Here!; Isabell, Here!. It didn't take long to learn that it was more pleasant to put your "Here!" in when your name was called and hold the cadence than to not answer and then be stared down by all those present as well as the dressing down by the officer in front of everyone.

Why am I thinking about all these things? Wasn't this day supposed to be set aside to think about Anna?

I also thought about the problem I'd experience when I would leave my practice in the Fringe country. There is such a "Big Wheel" of need here. So many are needed to help these people. The wheel seems to be turning in a cadence, a rhythm, calling out the kinds of people needed. I can hear the roll call as it says: "Nurse, Here!; Doctor, Here!; Agriculturist, Here!; Christian Missionary, Here!; Veterinarian! If I don't answer the roll call, the Big Wheel will stop. And everyone will glare at me. And what might the commanding officer say to me?

40

*When I go home to my Anna and we are married, how will
I tell her about the Big Wheel that is back in Ethiopia, so
many thousands of miles away. And what might she think
if I respond: Veterinarian, Here!?*

Neighbors to the East

Soon, it became possible to leave the clinic in the capable
hands of Ling. He had progressed so well and the people of
the area had accepted him readily.

This became apparent to me one day as I was resting after
worming a herd of sheep. A stranger came into the clinic,
looked around the room and asked if he could see Ling.

"Ling is outside at the back of the clinic," I told him. "I'm
Doctor Bill. Can I help you?"

"I kinda was looking for Ling because he treated my calf
last year and did so well," he replied, "that I was hoping he
could help me again."

This was a joy I could hardly believe! Ling was my friend,
my helper, my dependable driver, my instrument cleaner,
my Jeep washer, and my right-hand man. Now, he had
become my colleague, because this man said, "Let Ling help
me with my calf."

For several months I had wanted to go to Barter Store III but
didn't feel I could leave my practice long enough to make the
trip. Now, I could leave Ling in charge and feel comfortable
in doing so.

The public road to that outpost (Barter Store III) is right
down the center of the Fringe country area. It passes each of
the three Barter stores. Each of these stores has a telephone,
about the only ones in the whole area, except for Sal's family,
who probably have the only private home telephone.

The Barter stores are operated and owned by the
government headquartered in Addis Ababa. The ruling
Monarchy reaches all the way to this Fringe border of the
inhabited part of Ethiopia.

The good part about this government is that the Fringe
country is governed the least of all the areas of Ethiopia.
There are no public schools in the Fringe country, so it is
ninety percent illiterate. The ten percent who can read have
been sent to Christian Missionary schools. After their

41

schooling, they usually return home and teach the rest of their families and community the things they have learned in school.

I'm sure that many more people can read English than is reported but the government does not ask for such information. In my opinion, the Fringe country is the best place to live in all of Ethiopia because as it is said, "He that is governed least is governed best."

For quite sometime, I had heard that four Christian missionaries from the United States live near Barter Store III, and I had never met them. After thirty-seven miles of dusty roads in my Jeep, I arrived at two white houses, made of mud walls and sheet metal roofs. They stood side by side with a school house about twice the size of my clinic building next door.

I stopped the Jeep, got out, and made my way to the first house. All four missionaries met me at the door when they saw an American-looking man approaching.

"I'm Doctor William J. Isabell," I said. They immediately grabbed me and started hugging me until I almost lost my breath. They introduced themselves to me as Bob and Mary Johnson and Benson and Juliana Canteriette.

"What on earth ever brought a veterinarian to this country?" they asked, almost in unison. They had heard about an American veterinarian several miles away but did not have transportation to visit him.

"I came here almost two years ago," I replied, "and now I have a wonderful practice."

"But, how did you find this Fringe country?" asked Bob.

"A student from the Fringe country and I went to school together in Alabama," I explained, "and just before graduation he invited me to come to his country to set up a much needed practice.

"His name is Sal Salasie and today he is working in Agriculture and has helped me learn the customs and language of the people," I continued. "He has also provided me with a Jeep and lets me live in an old house and use an abandoned schoolhouse for my clinic."

"How is Sal?" they all asked together.

"The best in every way," I replied. "He's a good man, very intelligent, and the best friend I have in all of Africa!"

Bob seemed to want to tell me something. I could tell by the way he was studying my face. He seemed to be trying to organize the words he wanted to say, without saying too much.

"We have a sponsor in the United States who is anonymous by choice," he began. "You probably don't know it, but the house you live in and your clinic are also funded by the same person who sponsors us. Also, Sal was sent to the U.S. for his agricultural training by the same person.

Why didn't Sal ever tell me about this? I wondered.

The five of us talked about everything imaginable in the United States, especially about politics and football. We talked about football games that were played four and five years before.

It was so refreshing to visit with these fellow Americans. All too soon I had to leave them and travel the dusty, dirty, thirty-seven miles back to the clinic. Of course I went by the same road. It's the only one.

Camel Whinnying in Cadence

For nearly two years, Anna wrote me every day. The letters always arrived in groups of three, four, or five, but that didn't bother me. I read them over and over many times. One of my favorite letters had been read so many times, it finally frayed around the edges. The "frayed" letter described some of our wedding plans. I could feel Anna's contagious excitement everytime I read it. However, I had some plans I needed to share with her.

It was important to me that Anna return with me to the Fringe country, for at least one or two years. I had not pressured her in any way, and I thought she would be willing to give it a try. But, what if she should say, "No! That life is not for me!"

I had really grown to love my practice in the Fringe country. I loved Ling, Sal, Boaz, and had even developed an appreciation for the camels.

Since I knew Boaz was soon to leave for a trip to the Red Sea area, I decided to see if there was anything I could do to help.

"Hi, Boaz," I hollered as I approached his store. "Are you about ready to load your camels?"

43

"I sure am," he replied. "And I have three which need to be loaded with millet seed."

"I sure wish you would let me load one of them," I responded.

"Help me fix the cargo deck in place. We'll tighten the girth and then you can load one of them," he instructed.

After finishing the preliminary work, Boaz gave the command for the camel to kneel in the loading position. I put one large bag of seed on the cargo deck and the camel hardly noticed it. When I loaded the second bag, the camel started whinnying. After the third bag, the whinnying continued up to the sixth bag. All the time it intensified in loudness and raised in pitch.

"Boaz," I asked. "Would it be all right for me to unload one bag at a time, to see what kind of reaction is made when taking off the load."

Boaz nodded his approval and as I began unloading the bags, one by one, that old camel just played the whinnying scale down. When the last bag was taken off, there was silence. I learned a pretty good lesson from that old camel. It taught me, that like man, even the camels carry burdens and they recognize the burdens of life and beg for their removal.

With that lesson learned, I reloaded the cargo, and waved goodbye to Boaz. Then I went straight to the clinic to get started on my own burden.

It had been obvious that our cattle parasite program had lost some of its effectiveness.I questioned why I had to worm some of the cattle three and four times a year. Just when I thought the problem was whipped, it would raise its ugly head again. I had to continue the program since it was such a great help to all of the farmers in the area.

For three solid days I visited farms and checked out everything I could find for answers to the parasite problem. I drew a blank. I just couldn't pinpoint the problem.

I had one more investigative method, however, I wanted to try. I put some map paper on my drawing board and drew in every farm in the area, placing the fences, trees, barns, hills, lowlands, ponds, types of grass and types of soil. Surely the maps would tell me something as to why the intestinal parasites were so bad in some areas and absent in others.

Ling and I checked the cows as to which farms were negative and which were positive. By observing the information on the map, it became obvious that every farm which had a pond for the cattle's drinking water, had cattle infested with parasites.

I then checked the pond water by taking a sample about a foot from the top of the water. After examining the sample under the microscope, there was no evidence of parasites. Ling and I returned to a pond for more samples.

"Look at the cows drinking from the pond," I called to Ling. "Why didn't we think of it before. They're drinking the water from the top of the pond."

We took samples near the top of the pond and found many worm eggs when placed under the microscope. Since the parasite eggs are lighter than water, they float on the surface.

The mild warm temperature in the Fringe area causes ponds to be an incubator for parasites and brings heavy infestation to the cattle as they drink the water. The problem was then solved by putting fences around the ponds and watering the cows in running creek water, blue, clean water.

Anna and Bill Are Married

After nearly two years of separation, and anticipation, the time had finally arrived. Anna would meet me at the airport, about an hour's drive from her home.

The long trip from the Fringe country of Ethiopia to Alabama did not seem nearly so far or so long as I was constantly thinking about Anna. She is so beautiful. Her lovely, silky hair frames her cherub like face. Her eyes are bright and expressive. She has a slim, stunning figure. My Anna is beautiful, beautiful beyond words. And soon, I'll see her.

As I rushed into the terminal, there she was. I thought my heart was going to jump right through my chest. We ran to each other's arms and without saying a word, hugged each other so tight I thought we'd crush one another. Then, Anna began crying.

"Nothing is wrong, is it?" I asked.

"I'm crying because I'm so happy," she sobbed. "Seeing you and holding you close makes me sure about us getting married."

Then she cried so loudly I was afraid the people in the airport would think I was hurting her in some way. But deep inside, I took pleasure in her tears because they told me that Anna was truly the right girl for me. Hers were tears of joy and love.

We left the airport and drove to her home to visit with her family. We only stayed about an hour. We needed to be alone. We had so much catching up to do. We needed to talk about our wedding plans and our future life together.

"Bill," she began as she looked intently into my eyes. "I have something to tell you right now. I was not going to say anything until after the wedding, but I must tell you now," Anna said, then stopped to organize her words.

"What are you thinking about?" I inquired, still puzzled about such a big announcement.

"You know, when you left for the Fringe country, we agreed for you to go for one or two years," she explained, "then we would evaluate the situation after you returned."

"Yes, I remember. Go on," I encouraged her.

"Well, I have decided that I want to go back with you to this country of yours and try it for a year or two," Anna added. "If you think you still want to spend that much more time in Africa."

I grabbed her so quickly it scared her. With my arms around her, I felt a big sigh of relief at what she had told me.

"That's exactly what I'd like to do," I said. "I just didn't know how to ask you to go back with me. For some reason, I don't think I'd be happy with a rural veterinary practice here in the U.S."

We talked for nearly two hours and never once mentioned the wedding arrangements. Finally, the subject about the wedding was raised and the problems Anna had encountered between our two families. In our exchange of letters, both of us had agreed that we wanted a simple wedding, inviting our families and a few close friends.

"My family thinks we should have a big wedding," Anna said. "They want the whole country to know about our marriage and our settling down in a rural veterinary practice near them. They have no thoughts about a foreign

46

practice. Your family wants a small wedding of close friends who will congratulate the veterinary missionary and his new wife before sending them off to the mission field."

We sat silently musing over the situation. Then Anna broke the silence. "My family doesn't know that I've decided that if you want to go back to the Fringe country, I want to go with you. And now, we've decided to go to the mission field for a while. What are we going to tell them?"

"Anna, I think we have a way out!" I exclaimed. "For the next two weeks before the wedding, we must arrange to be away from our parents as much as possible. We will need to get many things to take back to the Fringe country. We'll just let our two families work out their own problems among themselves."

We both knew our families would never get the wedding off the ground without our help, but we decided to just let them do what they could. Then we'd step in to finalize the plans. Before long we found that a committee had been formed with three members from each family. That was a catastrophe from the start, because there was no tie-breaking vote.

In one instance, they voted on whether to have the wedding at Anna's home or at the church. The vote was three for each one. When we finally got into the act, Anna suggested that we have the wedding at the church and the reception at her home. Still no agreement. It was settled by a flip of a coin. We would have the wedding at home and the reception at the church.

On the day of our wedding, the phone rang constantly. "Is the wedding at your home or the church?" everyone asked. When Anna informed the callers, they each thought we had done it all backwards. "Well," Anna would explain, "We kind of wanted to be different, so we just did it backwards."

By two in the afternoon, everything was in place for the wedding. Anna was wearing a beautiful, long, white-laced gown which was worn originally by her Mother. I had rented a pale gray tuxedo with all the trimmings, and no telling who or how many wore it before me.

Two preachers were used for the ceremony because the "committee of six" voted three to three for each preacher. One performed the ceremony and was quite nervous — almost never getting through with the "I do's" and the "I will's" as he

47

glanced first to Anna, then to me. The second preacher was also very nervous as he gave the prayer of blessing and the benediction. I didn't think he would ever get through blessing us as he went over and over the same blessings.

Finally, the wedding ceremony was over — and the next activity on the program was the reception at the church, just two blocks away. Here, the committee had another difference of opinion. Some thought we should ride to the church, others believed we should just walk the two blocks. So, Anna's family passed us in their cars while my family walked along the sidewalk.

The reception went off without a hitch — except for my Grandmother who is an absolute "Teetotaler." She noticed someone pouring clear Champagne (slightly alcoholic) into the orange colored punch bowl and decided that she would make someone pay for that transgression.

"What is this?" she said very loudly pointing to the punch.

"This is fruit punch," someone answered.

"And what is this?" she insisted. "Does this bottle contain clear water?"

"Well, not exactly," was the honest reply.

She retreated but had clearly made her point.

Just before we left for our honeymoon, Anna rapped her spoon against a glass to get the attention of all family and friends.

"I would like to make an announcement to all of you," she began. "I'm making it rather than Bill because I am the one who made the decision that will effect all of our lives."

Everyone grew deathly silent as they waited expectantly for her important announcement.

"Following our honeymoon, we will be going to Bill's practice of veterinary medicine in the Fringe country of Africa for a one or two-year trial period."

Even in Anna's announcement our families were split. Anna's Mother cried! We wouldn't be in a rural practice close to home. My Mother smiled! We would be following in their footsteps as missionaries to Africa.

So we dodged the rice and drove off to our honeymoon!

Chapter Four

Mileage Culture Miracles Work

No Mileage Log or Charge

THE HEAT in the Fringe country can be almost unbearable at times. I suppose the camel is the only animal uniquely made for these conditions. The camel holds a particular fascination for me. So much so that poor Anna had to listen to my never ending accumulation of camel knowledge.

While much I learned would never be applied to my veterinary practice, I had an insatiable desire to have all the facts at hand should I need them. After all, the camel is the chief means by which it is possible for people to live in the desert, or to journey across them, like the one which is at the north boundary of the Fringe country.

The camel can drink thirty gallons of water in ten minutes. He kneels down to be loaded with cargo weighing as much as seven hundred pounds — but whinnies to his owner while being loaded. At a given command, despite the load and whinnying, he will slowly lift the load to his standing position. Though he may only walk at about two and one-half miles an hour, he can make twenty-five miles each day across the long, hot desert.

The destination across the Fringe country desert is the Red Sea. Here, the camel can take on more water. The humble camel doesn't seem to know, nor does it seem to bother him that the water of the Red Sea is salty. (All other animals cannot drink salt water). As a matter of fact, the salt water goes well with the bitter, thorny bushes he eats along the desert route. As this is the only food available in the desert, the camel eats what is at hand. The salt water and the thorny bushes don't give him indigestion, so he really doesn't need to care whether or not a veterinarian is in the caravan or not.

The cargo is carried up the desert area of the Fringe country to the Red Sea, through the northeastern section of the Sudan, and then across the Arabian Desert to be delivered near Cairo, Egypt, a distance of nearly 1,200 miles. After unloading the cargo, the camel is reloaded with goods needed in the Fringe country and tracks back over these same deserts toward home, steadily moving his broad, two-toed feet which keep him from sinking in the sand.

Often on the return route through the Arabian Desert, fierce wind currents caused by the varying elevations and fluctuating temperatures can be encountered. When a wind storm suddenly rushes in, the camel, without command, kneels to the ground in a crouched position, and closes his nostrils tightly to avoid the driving sand. His overhanging eye-lids also close tightly to protect his eyes from flying sand and wind. The rider cuddles down behind the camel's body and cargo. When the storm is over and all is well, the camel allows his rider to mount him again and they continue their trip to our community near Barter Store I.

Usually the cargo going to Cairo is cow hides and the return cargo is an improved strain of millet seed for planting. These improved millet seeds are under the direction of our agriculturist and community agent, Sal Salasi.

Perhaps the most interesting fact is that the transportation costs for this extended trip of nearly 2,500 miles or so is $0 — not one penny for gas, oil, or tire repair. The camel drinks sea water and eats thorny desert bushes. Protecting himself, the cargo and the rider from the storms, the camel provides an economical and safe round trip.

Stay Right Here — with Culture

On one trip to the States, my feelings were deeply hurt by well-meaning people who remarked, "Surely you and Anna don't want to live your lives in such a deserted place as Africa! How can you survive with so few telephones, poor roads, no automobiles or televisions, lack of schools and mostly because 'culture"'is totally absent from the peoples of the Fringe country?"

Though hurt, I would smile and nod politely about all the array of lacking items. It was true that I could go down the list and note each missing item they mentioned. I could agree that the list was true — many things were lacking — except one! Culture was certainly not lacking among the people of the Fringe country.

I wondered, what do these well-meaning people have in mind when they talk about culture? I supposed that by culture they meant the music, literature and art as might be viewed in a museum. And I was right.

On one occasion, I was driven along a sprawling Interstate to a museum in a plushly appointed automobile. There, I was shown an exhibit of beautiful paintings. (I enjoy beautiful pictures). They pointed out that the depth and dimension of every detail in the artistry brings out something "deep" inside each person who looks at them.

"Yes," I remarked. "Those are certainly beautiful pictures. And the frames, lighting and the building where they are displayed has made a wonderful trip for me." On the way back home, however, I wondered how much of that "culture" would really soak into my real self.

The real culture of the peoples of the Fringe country will never be housed in a museum. If we had such a magnificent building, we would not have the beautiful paintings. And even if we did, we wouldn't have a big Interstate highway or a plush automobile to take us to it.

The culture of the Fringe country is ancient. Much of it goes back to Bible times, like the story of Rebekah at the well, drawing water for the camels of strangers from distant lands, for her own camel, and for the camels of her friends. This pictures much more than "Rebekah at the well." It shows an inward culture rather than outward artistry.

The culture of the Fringe country people is simplistic. As an example, the many times I have answered a knock at the clinic door and find someone who has come for the doctor to see his sick cow. "Hello. Won't you come in?" I'd ask. "Not right now, thank you. I'll just wait right here," would be the reply. You see, he had been working all day and his clothes were dirty. His hands were dirty, but his heart was pure! His gesture to stay outside was his way of being respectful, polite and displayed a comfort deeper than the dirt on his clothes. To me, that is culture!

Six Thousand Miracles — the Camel

My camel practice made up only about one percent of my entire veterinary work. Yet, as you have no doubt gathered by now, my hobby time or recreational thinking was used in the study of the camel. I mentioned earlier about writing the school in Alabama where I had studied for information on the camel but received nothing. They had told me that they had no knowledge about this wonderful animal and did not think it was worthwhile to pursue its study. It was an insult to me and the camel, that needful information did not exist nor did anyone seem to care. I felt as though I should apologize to the camel and to the many friends I had made for the insults from my school.

Some documented information exists, however, about camels in the United States. In 1850, sixty camels were brought to the Southwestern United States, and were found to be very well adapted to life there. When the Civil War began, the United States gave up the camel project. Some of the camels escaped and turned wild. The settlers, afraid of them, shot them on sight. A few camels were seen as late as 1900, but became extinct as wild animals in North America.

I have accumulated more information about the camel than the veterinary school has where I graduated. But, what shall I do with all of it? Anna has repeatedly told me that I am obsessed with the camel, but by not sharing the information I have, I am doing a disservice to veterinary practices.

One night I had a most pleasant dream, and you guessed it, it was about camels. I did not tell Anna about it, although I did write it down so as not to forget it. The dream was about Job, a colorful character from the Bible who had six thousand camels.

"What did You have in mind, Lord, when You gave me all these camels?" Job asked the Lord.

"I knew you liked camels," the Lord answered.

"But Lord," Job continued, "One day we put these six thousand camels in a line, head to tail, and the line was six miles long!"

God then told Job about His plan. "We will have a circus show of camels with a maid servant and a man servant for each camel. Each of them shall be trained to do their performance. All the maid servants shall be like Rebekah, because of her purity and beauty, and because she made friends with the camel. Each camel shall be girthed tightly and the performance deck shall be robed with fine linen. I shall give you a new miracle — all six thousand camels shall finish their acts with their cargo intact and each shall go through the eye of a needle."

The entire show was overwhelming, done just as the Lord commanded. Job was astonished! He had never seen such a miraculous show as this.

"Why have You done these things for me?" Job asked.

"Because you are my trusted servant and I want to teach all people that which is given to one trusted servant shall be given to all peoples who trust in the Lord," the Lord concluded.

Suddenly, I awoke from my sleep and my vivid dream. It had all been so real. Truly it had been "The Greatest Show on Earth!"

Ling to Become a Vet

It was a very special day for me. I had some very good news to share. Ling had consented to go to the United States and enroll in Veterinary School. He had already been doing much of the same work as I did. I knew he wanted to be a veterinarian. I had mentioned it to him many times, but he only had given me a smile as his response. There had never been an answer or a commitment from him.

It took me some time to realize why Ling did not respond. I had told him that Dr. Mac, who lived in Tennessee, was my friend and would help him get accepted in school. I also told him that I would see to it that his entire expenses would be paid. Though the offer had been repeated many times, there was still no acceptance, no answer. There was always just his smile.

I learned that the problem with my proposal was that it was not exacting as was the custom of the Fringe people. For instance, if I asked Ling to ride with me to the post office, he would not go, unless I also told him he could ride back with me. You see, I had been telling him to go to school but I had failed to tell him that he would come back home.

Another problem that surfaced was that Ling was not sure he could qualify with the requirements to enter school. When he told me this, I also began to worry about it. I notified Dr. Mac that I needed a pre-entry examination form for a foreign student to enter a U. S. College. I told him to send it to the missionary school located near Barter Store III. The school could administer the examination and that would make it legal and proper. After it arrived, Ling took the test and passed it with flying colors. (The test was on the level of a high school graduate in the U.S.).

Dr. Mac had written that if we needed money for Ling's education he would be glad to share by giving half, if I would give the other half. This was a great gesture. But, what about my half? Where could I come up with that much money?

I decided to write the anonymous foundation in the U.S. which supported my clinic and the missionary school. I presented Ling as a qualified local young man, whom I needed to help me in the clinic, but needed to go to a Veterinary School in the U.S. Almost immediately, I received a reply. In a very business-like letter I was informed that Ling's expenses would be covered.

After I had read the good news and shared it with Ling, I began to have a secret thought. Now that Anna and I are married, I wonder if they would consider raising my support to take care of her now, or later, or even retirement. I wondered how rich they really were and whether they would

consider giving more towards Anna's support. But I thought
I had best leave "well enough alone!"

Chapter Five

Altitude Is Important

A Camel Specialist — Some Day!

ANNA AND I AGREED that because of the expense and timed involved in returning to the U.S., we would take a two month furlough every two years. We had lived and practiced our veterinary medicine in the Fringe country for twenty-two months and then left to spend our two months in the Southeastern U.S. near her family on Sand Mountain, Alabama.

We had planned our furlough so I could attend the American Veterinary Medical Association (AVMA) which was meeting in a large midwestern town during our time home. I had secretly dreamed about being on the program someday. The list of distinguished speakers always includes specialists on swine and cows, and continues to go on to include dogs, horses, sheep and goats. But, the list always stops short of a camel specialist. Each specialist has a doctorate in his own field.

Of course, I don't claim to be a camel specialist, except where I live in the Fringe country. There, I am a specialist, even though I live in a little white mud house with a tin roof near Barter Store I. You can see that it would be virtually

57

impossible, as well as impractical to ever have a camel specialist speak at the AVMA.

During a break between sessions, I became better acquainted with two doctors sitting near me in the back of the room.

"Where do you practice?" asked one of the doctors.

"I practice in the Fringe country of Ethiopia in Africa," I replied.

"My, my! What do you do? Is it all monkey business?" the other doctor jested.

Even though I knew he was only kidding, I did not like his remark. "I have never seen a monkey where I live," I told him. As a matter of fact, in all the time I have spent in Africa I have not even seen any monkeys.

"My practice is worming cattle," I continued. "And before you turn off this simple practice, hear me out. Before I came to the Fringe country, none of the cows or calves had ever been wormed and those poor farmers were loosing about half of their herds from intestinal parasites. Now, by worming each of them yearly, we have not lost a single calf through this infection. If you boys were to keep tabs on our production now, you would see how much better off we are today," I concluded.

By this time, the circle of doctors surrounding me had grown and they were all listening intently to everything I was saying. It was like dropping a stone in the middle of a pond and noticing the ripples of water as it went toward the shore. I was the stone and all the doctors began surrounding me sat in ripples listening to all I had to say.

"In the Fringe country, we have very little feed for our cattle and the nutritional value of the feed is very low," I continued speaking to my attentive, growing audience. "Our motto is 'Keep the worms out!' Your cows in this country are well fed and you pay very little attention to worming. Usually you are able to produce some pretty fat cows. If you were to worm your herds well, you'd produce some really fat cows."

One of the vets who was listening intently raised his hands and like being in a Sunday church service, said, "Amen, doctor!"

"My concern is for the little farmer in our Fringe area. We have a number of farmers with only one cow. They are so humbled by their plight that they really don't expect me to help them," I explained. "When I have the opportunity to help one of them by caring for their single cow, I am really helping to treat that man's self-esteem also. Personally, I believe that if any doctor is not willing to serve the little farmer in anyway, his license to practice should be revoked immediately!"

Our rap session was interrupted by the moderator's gavel at the podium. "Sometimes the wisdom during the intermission is more profound than the program speakers," he said. "How many of you would like to hear more from the African doctor?" he asked. A resounding round of applause stunned me while the moderator motioned for me to come to the podium.

By the time I reached the platform my mind was so stunned I could think of nothing to say. I fumbled with a glass of water on the podium while I shot up a quick prayer for guidance.

Lord, I'm in a pickle, I admitted. *What shall I say?*

Almost immediately the Lord told me to relate some of my experiences as a missionary veterinarian and then close with the dream about Job's camels. I had never told anyone, not even Anna, about the dream. *Would it be all right to tell it here?* The Lord seemed to tell me that He would be with me and would not let the story fail. Suddenly, I felt much better!

After a few minutes of information about my work in the Fringe country, I told the attentive audience, "I am a lover of camels, or maybe I should say that I am infatuated with camels. I have read everything I have been able to find about the camel, even though my practice to camels is only about one percent of my business. But, let me tell you about a dream I had several months ago in my place of service," I began.

My colleagues sat in rapt attention as I reiterated the miracle of Job's six thousand camels and the dialogue between him and the Lord. Many of the doctors knew something about the Bible and the dream seemed to make the book come alive. I concluded with, "Truly, this was the 'Greatest Show on Earth.'" Then I thanked my audience for their attention and went to sit down. Scores of my fellow veterinarians came to me, shaking my hand and thanking me for such an inspiring talk.

When things quieted down I thought, *Lord, You made such a hit with your "camel miracle." I think that it was You who put the camel on the program today and at the same time, You placed Yourself in the hearts of many of the people here.*

Maybe this whole thing was another step for me in my quest to become a "camel specialist."

A Fine Name for a Puppy

No sooner had we returned to the Fringe country, Sal came excitedly to the clinic. He had some wonderful news to share with me.

"Because the farmer in our area have so many needs," he began, "the foundation in America is sending money to the clinic and also to my agriculture program," he related with a big smile on his face.

Actually, the application and other information needed by the foundation had been submitted several months earlier, but I knew nothing about it and Sal had never mentioned it to me. He was so very true to the culture of his people. No one in the Fringe country ever gives a hint of any happening until all is signed, sealed and delivered. Even the children have secret plans and ideas but they never share them until they are fully developed.

We were delivering puppies by Caesarean section one day and three little boys came by to see what kind of animals were in the clinic. After the operation, each of the puppies were doing fine and the mother was resting in her recovery pen. There were four white females and one black male.

"I'd like to take that little black puppy home with me," exclaimed Tad, one of the three youngsters who had been observing the operation.

"Only if you wait until weaning time," the owner answered.

"That's fine with me," Tad said excitingly. So the little black puppy would have a new home after eight weeks weaning time.

One day, nearly a year later, I noticed some small figures coming in the direction of the evening wind, across the hot desert sand. The clouds looked like it could rain at any time. In the Fringe country there are days when every kind of weather imaginable comes within the same twenty-four hours.

Through the haze I noticed that there were three small children, a dog and a ladder being carried by a boy at each end. As they came closer, I recognized the ring-leader as Tad, the little boy who asked for and got his black puppy.

"Do you remember this dog?" Tad asked, pointing to his proud prize, while speaking for all three boys.

"Isn't that the little black puppy you got here at the clinic about a year ago?" I answered.

"Yes sir," Tad replied. "You do remember the pup, don't you? His name is John."

"That's a fine name for a dog," I said with a smile.

"Go get Ling and Miss Anna and we will show you something," Tad commanded. "Go get them and you will see."

I went to get Anna and Ling, even though the skies looked threatening. I wondered how long it would be before the rain would begin and we would all be caught in a down pour.

"Sit in a straight line and look in the direction of the big open space," Tad instructed us.

John, the little black dog was commanded to "Sit up!" and up he went on his two hind legs. Next he was told to "Play dead," and the little black puppy laid over on his side with his eyes closed. Then Tad threw a ball and commanded John to "Fetch the ball." Immediately, little John ran, retrieved the ball and brought it back to the boys. On another command, Tad told John to "roll over" and over the pup went.

Then came the grand finale! The other two boys held the ladder upright while Tad put little John at the bottom of one side of the ladder. When Tad gave the signal, the little black dog began climbing the rungs, one at a time, until he had reached the top of the ladder. Tad held out his arms and John jumped from the top of the ladder into his arms.

Anna, Ling and I clapped our hands to show our appreciation for the boy's fine training and the intelligent dog's obedience.

"Thank you very much," we all said in unison. Then Anna invited the boys into our little house for millet meal cookies before they left for home. By this time, the clouds were thickening and the wind showed heavy signs of impending rain.

Within thirty minutes after the boys left, we saw them coming toward the clinic again. This time each of the boys seemed to be carrying little John — at least each of them had one hand on his body.

"What's the matter?" I asked. "Is little John sick?"

"Oh no," the boys said. "He was too tired to walk back to your house so we are carrying him. We forgot one trick we taught him which will finish his act."

Little John was placed on the ground and when the signal was given, he raised his right paw and waved it in the air, telling us "goodbye."

Heavy rain began to fall as Tad and his two friends, and little John, ran toward their home nearly a mile away.

The Camel is Too Tall — Get a Ladder

It was an especially happy day. Ling was back home after finishing his schooling. He held his deluxe sheep-skin diploma in his hand.

"I see that you have a very beautiful diploma in your hand," I teased him. "Now let's go to work and see how much knowledge you have in your head."

Ling's only answer was a big smile. I knew that he was well prepared to climb any mountain in his field of practice. It was good to have him back to work in the clinic with me, proud of his accomplishments. He would become a very efficient co-worker in my practice of veterinary medicine.

Anna was happy that day also! She was waiting for two orphan goats to come to our clinic for a visit. Each spring some of the farmers in the area had nanny goats which die giving birth to their kids. Anna enjoyed taking these little goats and with a bottle and sheep nipples, feed them all summer until they were old enough to go home and eat grass at their own farm. I, too, loved to watch the little goats. They were so gentle and easy to give their bottles.

The little goats were so friendly that you could hardly walk, work, stand, or rest, and there they were, ready to love you to death. All the children in our community would come to the clinic and wait in line just to give the little goats their bottles of milk.

Of course, Anna and I never did seem to have enough milk for all the goat feedings, so we would just pour water into the bottles, mixed with a little milk. The little goats would drink until their sides were bulged out and bloated. Though it was mostly water, it didn't hurt them. They were all right.

It was a happy day! Anna was happy. Ling was happy! The goats were happy! The little children were happy! I suppose the one thing that would make my day as happy as theirs would be to get a call from someone to visit a camel. I wouldn't want the camel to be too sick, or too mean, or too far away. Because of my admiration for the camel, *it would bring me much happiness if I could doctor one today*, I thought.

The Lord must have read my thoughts because Boaz, the biggest camel owner in the area, had just come into the clinic.

"Hello Boaz," I greeted him. "What brings you here today?"

"Mr. Camel Doctor," he replied, "I need your help with one of my camels."

We got into the Jeep and headed toward Boaz' house. On the way he kept talking about his camels and I listened intently, learning all I could about his herd.

"I know what's wrong with my camel," Boaz said. "He just can't seem to get any relief.

"What do you mean?" I asked.

"Well, you see, his rear part is stopped up and he can't seem to get any relief."

"Oh yes," I replied. "That is called rectal impaction and is quite common among several species of animals."

"You know," Boaz continued, "In Bible times and even today, most camels who had this problem went to the edge of the sea and would sit down in the water for as long as ten days. They would let the water soften and wash the trouble away."

I thought that it was probably true that the camel sat in the water, letting the impaction soften, but he probably had to "bump" his rear end against the bottom. After several hours, or even days, he would probably get some relief. I didn't want to tell him, but Boaz was a camel specialist and he didn't know it.

When we reached Boaz' house, he led me back to the camel lot, where I saw his oldest and most trusted camel standing with both hind legs spread wide apart. The rectum was packed and bulged to an extent I had never seen. I got a large bucket of millet seed oil, which is very bland, soothing and penetrating. After washing my hands, I lubricated my right arm all the way to my shoulder.

The camel was twice as tall as I was and the only way I could reach his rectum was to have the camel lie down. I tried to get Boaz to have the camel to lie down.

"I've tried to get him to go down," Boaz informed me. "He just can't do it. But I will try one more time."

Boaz gave the familiar command but the big camel just whinnied and continued to hold his hind legs wide apart.

Dear Lord, I said to myself. *What can I do? I can't reach that troubled spot of this camel.*

"Get me a ladder!" I yelled. Boaz and one of his hired hands brought a ladder and together they tried to hold it upright, slightly leaning it against the rear end of the camel.

I climbed the ladder and reached the needed height. All of sudden I thought about my good friend back in the U.S., Dr. Mac. *What would he think if he saw me now? He would probably laugh a little, but he would certainly call me a "camel specialist."*

After several minutes of cleaning the impacted material from the camel's rectum, the lubricating oil seemed to sooth the troubled patient. While coming down the ladder, the old camel needed to flex his legs slightly and while doing so, he knocked the ladder out from under me. I fell to the ground but it was only a short fall and I suffered no injuries. What did get the best of me was my Southeastern U.S. temper which flared up immediately. In my anger, I hit the dear old camel on the rear with one of the instruments I had in my hand.

Suddenly, there was extreme quietness among the small group that had gathered to watch me work. A definite coldness was felt among the crowd and I carried it home with me. Boaz had always treated me warmly and thanked me graciously for my help. He always gave me millet seed

64

as payment for my services and we always parted as dear, warm friends. But this time, the warmth was absent. A coldness prevailed!

I went straight to Sal's house. I told him about my experiences with the camel and my temper tantrum when the camel knocked me off the ladder. I asked why the sudden coldness I felt from Boaz and the crowd. He immediately knew the answer.

"You insulted a sacred camel of Boaz' household," Sal told me. "When you struck the camel, it was like striking one of the venerated members of his family."

Sal went on to tell me a story about Boaz and his camels. He said that Boaz and his wife are from the ancestral lineage of Abraham, Sarah, Isaac and Rebekah. When Isaac and Rebekah were married, the camel was a symbol of "purity" for their marriage. The camel was considered sacred and was a symbol of their faith to each other.

He related the biblical story of the search for Isaac's wife when Abraham sent his trusted servant to a kindred land to find a pure virgin for his son. The servant took ten camels and was to go to a certain well and wait for a very fair damsel to come draw water for her family. When Rebekah saw the stranger, she offered to draw water for him, and also for all his camels. Abraham's trusted servant knew immediately that this beautiful virgin was to be Isaac's wife. Rebekah rode nearly four hundred miles on a trusted camel to meet her new husband to be, Isaac.

When I returned home, Anna could sense my despondency. I related the incidents of the day to her and concluded with the story that Sal had told me. She took me in her arms and held me close while she told me that she was my "Rebekah."

Early the next morning, I drove to Boaz' house and asked him to call all the people together who were present while I treated his camel the day before. When they were all present, I humbly apologized for my behavior and asked them for their forgiveness. Their smiles, handshakes and hugs assured me that I was forgiven. Boaz and I became very close friends and all those in my household and his were warmly grateful for each others friendship.

They Called Us
"Mr. Cow Doctor" and "Miss Screen Wire Anna"

Though Anna and I had been married for more than a year, I have said little about the "newly weds," mostly because it would seem too "mushy." But the "love-birds" are still deeply in love, even though the honeymoon is over. I knew for sure that Anna was the right one for me and that I was the right one for her.

From the moment she arrived in the Fringe country, Anna was received as a "know-how" lady among the women. Her training in home economics was put into practice and she was welcomed warmly by the women when they sewed together and talked about cooking. Soon Anna had learned six ways to make bread from millet meal and about ten ways to make cakes from the same meal. That's a lot of bread and cake to eat everytime she tried a new recipe.

When Anna would come home from one of the sewing classes, she always talked to me about the homes of her friends. Most of their houses did not have screen door and the flies and insects which came into their houses were a potential danger to their health. This was particularly true in the Fringe country where there is a mild climate and the winter temperature never gets below freezing.

One night Anna and I talked about the sickness in our area and she remembered a similar situation near her home in Sand Mountain, Alabama. Every summer there had been a rage of "Typhoid fever," but her family of eleven members never had the disease. Anna said that most of the doctors in the community thought that the reason her family evaded the disease was because their mother cooked three hot meals a day and that the large family ate every bit of them. There was never any food left over to be eaten later. And, there were no flies to infest any left over food because they had screens on their doors and windows.

We decided that we would begin a campaign in the community around Barter Store I, and emphasize two points: Get screens on the windows and screen doors that closed tightly and every meal was to be cooked hot. Anna got to work on her project immediately and finally lost count on the number of houses she had screened and the number of stoves she made to heat up three times a day.

There was a group of people who lived to the east of us and who could speak very little English, only enough to get by. When they came to our house, we greeted them warmly and asked how we could help them. When they came, if they did not want me, "Mr. Cow Doctor," they asked for "Screen Wire Anna." They meant that they wanted Anna to help them get screen wire for their house. So, around the Isabell household, there were two persons: "Mr. Cow Doctor" and "Miss Screen Wire Anna."

Absolutely! Make the Goat Barn Low

One day Anna wiped the tears from her eyes and said, "This stops today!" She had determined not to take in any more orphan kids because it was so hard to give them up when we took them back to their owners. For nearly a year, Anna had fed the cute little, loving goats with a bottle and nipple.

The climax finally came when I asked her if she wanted to ride with me while I took her little friends back to their owner. She agreed and the four of us got into the Jeep. I tried to quiet her feelings by assuring her the little goats would be happy to join the other larger goats in the owner's pasture. When we arrived at the farm several miles down the road from our house, no one was home. I picked the little fellows out of the Jeep and put them in the pasture, just inside the fence.

When I got back into the Jeep, started the motor and began moving slowly away, we both looked back at the little goats. They ran along the fence line after the slow moving Jeep, crying, bleating and begging for us not to leave them. Anna cried all the way home.

"Why don't we get a couple of nanny goats and one billy goat," I asked, trying to comfort Anna. "Then we could raise our own goat family." There was nothing but silence.

"I know some people who live to the east who have several goats," I continued. "Let's go see if we can get some goats from them."

This family spoke an English-Hebrew dialect. I knew that talking to them would be difficult. But, maybe I could get them to understand me. Sure enough, they had just the right goats for us and agreed to let us have them. The owner explained that the goats would need a little barn like his, pointing in the direction of his goat barn. It had a flat roof which was several feet above the ground.

"When we bring the goats to you, we will also bring the materials to build you a barn," the owner explained.

"That's fine," I replied. "I'll see you in the morning."

Early the next morning the goat farmer and his boys were at our place with the goats and started to build the barn for us. Before leaving for the clinic, I told the older man not to make our barn as high as his.

"Oh no!" he exclaimed. "Must make the barn high."

"No! No! Make it short," I replied, holding my hands down to approximately three and one-half feet.

"Make it high," he insisted.

"Absolutely no!" I said finally. "Absolutely make it low!"

When I returned from the clinic later in the evening, the barn was built just as I had instructed with the desert grass twinned together for a roof. The goats were under the new barn. Anna went with me for the inspection. We both looked with pleasure at our family of goats and their new barn.

The next morning, we went out to see our goats. The goat farmer had been right! The barn should have been built "very tall" because the goats had climbed on top of their new barn and had eaten the grass roof. With a roofless barn the goats were having their second meal while chewing their "cud."

Not So Bad to be the Goat

When it came to the important things in life, I had never found Anna to be wrong. She seemed to have an uncanny sense about people and things, and could usually put them in perspective. But when it came to my feelings about animals, she seemed to take a defensive position.

She told all our friends that my love and priorities in life were Anna, the camel, and the goat — in that order. Jokingly, she said she was afraid to ask me to put them in the order of my love, afraid that she would be the last on the list, or even left out all together. But, everyone knew how deeply I loved Anna. But they also knew about my love for the camel.

I suppose Anna was right about my third choice in my priorities. It was the goat, because it is probably the most valued animal among mankind, with the exception of the camel. More than one hundred million people in the world are dependant on the camel for their survival in the deserts and its surrounding territories.

The goat, however, is more valuable for its milk production than the cow, and has sometimes been called the "poor man's cow." It chews the cud like a sheep and is useful for its milk, wool, meat and hide. It has provided meat and milk for people since Bible times.

Most domestic goats weight about one hundred pounds. The most popular breeds for wool production are the Angora and Cashmere. Goats are swift footed and suitable for mountain life. The Rocky Mountain goat is the best mountain climber in the United States. With little protection, they can survive the wilds of the wilderness.

Another wonderful quality of the goat is that they can be used as children's pets because of their gentle disposition and quickness in training.They can be easily taught to pull a wagon and can be managed by children. Goats love the taste of metal and are sometimes accused of eating tin cans. They often lick holes in the bottoms of their metal feed containers.

While visiting with Miss Bessie in the U.S. once, I got a call to treat a goat. Mr. Mason, who lived in an old service station on the highway near her, called to ask if I could treat his goat for a minor injury from a harness rub, caused by pulling a small goat wagon.

When I arrived at the old service station, a highway patrolman was parked near the driveway, checking traffic speed with his radar equipment. The patrolman's presence seemed to be slowing Mr. Mason's business. He wanted me to treat his goat quickly so he could let him loose.

As soon as the goat was treated, he heard the squelching noise of the patrol radio and went straight for the car. He jumped up on the hood of the patrol car and began licking the expensive radar equipment. The patrolman scared the goat away, got back into his car and then drove away. The area became quiet as the goat had completed his assignment.

Chapter Six

Random Thoughts and Experiences

Tired Before They Start

When in the Fringe country, eight thousand miles away from home, Anna and I sometimes got homesick. Usually, after we received a letter from our folks back home, our thoughts would turn to them and the radical differences we were experiencing. Even my veterinary practice was so very different.

Of course, the cattle herds in the U.S. are much larger. I remember, while on furlough once, I helped my friend, Dr. Mac, at his clinic in Robertson County, Tennessee. Even though we had gone to school together and both of us practiced veterinary medicine, there were so many obvious differences.

While I was with him we used a Practice Truck which had a two-way radio, connecting communication with his office every minute of the day. We traveled paved roads and everyone called him by telephone when there was a need. And then there were all kinds of forms he had to fill out which were required by the government.

Dr. Mac, licensed by the State of Tennessee to do his veterinary work, is required to keep up his continuing education. He has a cattle chute which is attached to his truck

71

to load and hold the cattle for transportation. He also had the competition of another six vets in his area, as well as several other distinctives I probably don't know about.

In the Fringe country, I did not have any large herds of cattle. There were no two-way radios or hard-top, paved roads. Sometimes the desert roads were only places where your tire tracks went. There were no telephones in homes, no government forms to fill out, no state vet licenses and no continuing education requirements. I did not have a cattle chute to drag around, nor any other competing veterinarians. But, I did have a Practice Jeep, about the only modern convenience comparable to Dr. Mac.

Most of the vets in the U.S. work themselves to fatigue, just trying to catch a scared cow to treat. I didn't have that problem. The cows in the Fringe country had never been stuck with a needle, so most of them trusted everyone.

Perhaps I should not try to compare my camel practice because the camel population in the U.S. is zero and there are no camel specialists. But, I was glad to be a camel doctor in the Fringe country of the continent of Africa.

A Rich Man

As a small boy, I liked to think of myself as being rich someday. The only rich man in the part of the country where I grew up was Mr. Leigeber. He was an automobile dealer in town.

At the beginning of World War I, this man of German descent placed a picture of the German leader in a prominent place at his dealership. It showed his obvious allegiance to the Kaiser. None of the folks said anything to Mr. Leigeber, they just quit buying his new cars. He got the message! In less than two weeks he took down the Kaiser's picture and placed American flags in every corner of his showroom.

After thinking about what the U.S. had done for him, Mr. Leigeber really changed. He could be seen pledging allegiance to our country's flag at every opportunity. His German dialect was always present, but we always knew Mr. Leigeber was a good American citizen.

He did so well selling his new cars that he decided to build a new showroom and sales office. The large plate glass in the front of the showroom had to be shipped by rail and in those early days, a pair of mules and wagon delivered such materials from the railroad. As the mules made their way up the cobblestone street, the large plate glass slipped from the wagon and broke into several large pieces. The driver went to apologize to Mr. Leigeber and ask him what he should do.

"Pick up every piece," he told the driver. "And take the pieces to the body shop."

The next printing of the weekly newspaper had an advertisement stating: "Plate Glass for Sale — cut to your needed dimension." All the glass was sold and Mr. Leigeber made a handsome profit.

Nothing Sick! Just Wanted to Talk!

When on furlough in the U.S., I usually liked to practice in Dr. Mac's clinic. It gave me an opportunity to catch up on the latest techniques and to treat animals which do not live in Africa. Dr. Mac and his family would spend several weeks out West to visit some big cattle ranches and I had the privilege to take care of his practice while he was gone.

I got a strange call one day from a man who was in poor health and yet needed a veterinarian to come to his large farm. I asked a service station attendant for directions to the man's farm and found out that he had been confined to his home with a terminal illness for several years, and that he was a wealthy man.

After arriving at Mr. Rainwater's house, I pressed the doorbell and heard its ring inside. I waited for someone to come to the door and finally heard a man's voice.

"Come on in!" he said. "I'm in here," he continued from an adjacent room. It was a very beautiful, well-built house.

"I'm Dr. William J. Isabell from Dr. Mac's clinic," I introduced myself. "I am here to help you with your animal."

"I'm glad to see you," Mr. Rainwater said as he tried to sit up in his bed. "But, won't you please sit down for a moment and talk with me for a little while?"

73

"Sure. I would enjoy talking with you very much," I said.

"Since you are a vet," he began, "I wish you would pick out some animal and tell me about it.

"Well, how about — how about — me talking about the camel?"

"You don't have to pick out an animal no one knows anything about," Mr. Rainwater answered.

"Well, sir," I replied. "I would like to say that I am a camel specialist."

"Great! Great!" he replied. "Tell me about the camel."

I must have talked at least fifteen minutes, describing the camel, mentioning that the camel has the longest existing record of service to man in the world. I also included the biblical accounts of the camel as a gift to Abraham, and Job's herd, and finally concluded that the camel brought the wise men to the stable where Christ was born,.

Everything was quiet for a while. Mr. Rainwater seemed to be trying absorb all the information I had given him.

"Where is the animal you need me to treat?" I interrupted his thoughts.

"Oh, I'm sorry! I have no animal to treat today," he said apologizing. "My medical doctors have done all that medical science knows to do for my condition. They have ordered me to invite several people in to talk with me as therapy," he explained. "Tell your clinic clerk to just bill me for your time, as if you had treated one of my animals."

He reached for something in the table drawer next to his bed and after writing for a short time, put the scrap of paper into an envelope. "Here's something for you, personally," he said and we made our goodbyes.

Before going to bed that evening, I opened the envelope which had a check for my missionary clinic in Africa. There was enough money to care for my clinic needs for an entire year.

I thought, *this may have been the highest paid "camel call" on earth!*

Sit-Ins, Long Walks and Bus Ridin'

When we are on furlough in the U.S., Anna and I usually live in one of the tenant houses on "Miss Bessie's" farm. My mother-in-law really knows how to run a farm. She has a simple philosophy: Just treat everyone as right as you can and everything will be all right.

All seven of her tenant houses are in good repair, with fresh paint and good roofs on them. There are adequate barns and they are each located conveniently near a good road on the eighty acre tract. Her tenant houses are not lined in a row, side by side, like many adjacent farms. She believes this is both degrading and embarrassing to the families who are living under such circumstances.

The most enjoyable pasttime Anna and I had on furloughs was to drive around the countryside and to the towns nearby to where we had been raised. It was interesting to see how some of the towns changed and others were still the same, year after year. While driving to one of our favorite towns one day, we were surprised to come upon a police roadblock, just before we got to the city.

The police officer stopped our car and asked for our driver's license, which I had kept renewed and up-to-date. He looked in the car and then asked Anna and I to get out and stand side by side. After studying my driver's license he asked me to recite the information printed on my license.

"Your name sir?" he asked authoritatively. I repeated my name and he went on to ask my age, height, and my address.

I gave the address of my Mother-in-law's farm and then he asked a question that had never been asked of me before.

"What did you say was the color of your skin?"

"It is a clear, white complexion," I answered.

"Well, you answered everything perfect, except the color of your skin," he said.

"Oh," I replied. "That is easy to explain. I am a missionary veterinarian to the Fringe Country of Ethiopia in Africa, which is located very near the hot desert sand. The heat has darked my skin during the years I have been there."

The officer was puzzled. Perhaps he thought we were trying to trick him with our answers.

"Well, I've never heard of a veterinarian in Africa who treated little dogs, horses and cows," he confessed. "And you are saying that is the reason your skin is so dark?"

I was still unaware as to why we were being questioned so much. But, I sensed that his detaining us was getting serious. I shot a quick prayer to the Lord. *Lord, I need a little help now. What shall I say?*

"Officer," I said politely, "I am a camel doctor!"

"Well, they do have camels in the desert and I guess they need doctors for them too," he answered. "But before you go, I'll tell you why we have these road-blocks. There are a lot of outside foreign people who have come here and are involved in sit-ins, long walks, and bus ridin' disturbances."

Anna and I did not understand what the officer was talking about, but we wanted to get away from there as soon as possible. I doubt that "Miss Bessie" had even heard about these "problems," — at least she hadn't told us about them.

By the time we got into the town, we noticed a large crowd of people around the restaurant on Main Street. There were policemen with hard-hats and everywhere we looked we saw angry people shouting and shoving around the crowded restaurant. Apparently, some were being denied service at the restaurant. The whole town was in an uproar. We found it hard to understand. Having spent the past several years in the Fringe country, we certainly didn't have anything compared to this. We went home, but didn't tell Miss Bessie about any of the things we had seen.

The next day we drove to another favorite town, about eighty miles away, and we encountered a similar circumstance. There we saw policemen surrounding a large circle of people. I took Anna by the hand and we innocently walked inside the circle to see what was happening. As we stopped to observe, we heard the "click" of a camera lens.

On our way home we noticed another vehicle following us along the highway. Everytime we slowed our speed, the car behind us slowed down. When we increased our speed, it also increased. As we reached our driveway, the unmarked car sped by with two uniformed policemen in it.

The next day we found our picture in the newspaper with the caption describing us as "Outside Agitators in the Latest Uprising in the Community!" The truth was that we were trying to see what the uprising was. We still could not determine the cause of the disturbance in this little county seat in Alabama.

With our picture in the newspaper, we thought it best to go talk with Miss Bessie. She said she knew about all the demonstrations but never let them interfere with the operation of the farm or her relationship with her neighbors and tenants.

"Let me tell you about the way I try to run this farm," Miss Bessie began. "I try to treat my tenants like I would want to be treated. Every year I give one hundred dollars to each young person who will go to college, and I do this every year they continue to go.

"At the end of every year, I take my large, blue, bookkeeping ledger to each of my tenants and sit down with one of the smart young people and their parents. I show them the year's operation of expenses and income, then divide the profits between them and myself. They know that I am being honest and fair.

"Then, I look around to see if there are any needed repairs on their house and volunteer to get everything in top order for the coming year. By being honest and working together, this farm makes more money for all of us than any other farm around these parts," she concluded.

There was a long silence! Each of us sat in contemplation and occasionally looked toward each other. Finally, I broke the silence.

"Miss Bessie," I began. "Anna and I think it would be best if we cut our furlough short and returned to the Fringe country. We think it is best if we leave right away," I concluded.

"Well children, I hate to see you go, but for your own safety, it may be best since you have been labeled as agitators. But, please don't worry about me. I'll be all right," she confided. There was another long silence!

"Let me tell you one more thing," Miss Bessie began. "I am not going to apologize for this preaching I am about to do, but please listen carefully.

"Once there was a man who was 'up a tree.' He was a short man and he was also short in dealing with people. He was conniving, stingy, and rich by taking advantage of other people. One day Christ came by the tree and told him to come down. This man said, 'Lord, if I have taken unjustly from anyone, I shall repay him four-fold.'"

The Lord said, "I shall go to your house and dine with you and I shall be a friend of all your household."

"Many of my neighbors are up in that tree," Miss Bessie continued, "because of their wrong doing in treatment of other people. We don't know what will happen in this country before all of them come down from the tree and begin to do things like the Lord commanded them. But, please don't worry about me. I have been kept in the safety of the Lord all the time."

We left for the airport the next morning. Before we boarded our flight, however, we asked the Lord's blessings and guidance for our troubled homeland.

Paint Can Make a Difference

The Fringe country is the best place in all Ethiopia to live. We have the greatest freedom in all of Africa, mostly because we are not a threat to the Communist type of government that had come to power. They usually were only interested in the big farming areas. The people of the Fringe country were mostly one cow, one goat, one camel operations.

The day came, however, when we began to feel the pressure for this great freedom, since the army, headquartered in Addis Ababa, was getting closer and closer to us. Actually, the peoples of the Fringe country were not great minds, had little power or money, and certainly did not pose a threat to anyone in the whole world.

One day, Sal and I went to a community to the west of us to check on some agricultural tests he had made earlier in the year. The pastures had been seeded with improved grasses and a new improved millet seed had been planted. I was going to check on the cattle in the area for the Spring parasite program.

The road we used had been in existence for many years, but the Spring rains had washed out several spots and made them almost impassable, but I was driving my new Jeep-like vehicle. The new vehicle had been made by the communists and was painted the same color as all their vehicles in our part of the world — army khaki. I slid into a deep ravine before I could control the Jeep. After trying for several minutes to get out of the ditch, Sal and I knew we would have to get some help.

We saw a group of local men working in a field nearby, but when we tried to approach them, they ran from us. Even though Sal, a native of the country pleaded with them, they continued to run. Then we saw an old American Jeep coming up the road in our direction. As soon as the driver saw us, he quickly turned around and headed in the opposite direction.

Sal and I looked puzzlingly at each other. Then Sal seemed to sense the reason for our dilemma.

"We are riding in this new vehicle, exactly like the army uses," he explained. "These people think we are army officials and have come to harass them. They run from us as soon as they see this vehicle."

"What can we do?" I asked. "How can we let them know who we are?"

"Let's start walking and find a farm which is out of sight from our Jeep," he suggested.

We found a farm just over the rise and were greeted cordially by the owner. He invited us in for a snack and water while we explained our situation to him. The three of us headed out for our vehicle, along with his two camels who made quick work of pulling us out of the ditch. We thanked him and he apologized for his neighbors refusal to help us. After seeing our vehicle, he told us that his neighbors must have thought we were the army. After finishing our assignments, we returned home with no trouble.

Two days later, as Anna looked out the window toward the clinic, she asked "Why are you driving your old Jeep today?"

"Do you think it looks like the old Jeep?" I asked.

"It sure does!"

"Well, my mission is accomplished!" I said.

Sal and I painted the new Jeep to look like the old one and so it served us better.

Chapter Seven

Ninety Degrees Awry — Misfit Go Home

Camel's Leg at Ninety Degree Angle

WHEN I FIRST CAME to the Fringe country, I operated the clinic by myself and it was very hard to take a day off from work. Now that Ling had his degree and was a full-fledged veterinarian, my work was not as demanding.

Anna had packed a lunch and we decided that we would visit our four Christian missionary friends near Barter Store III. They had told us that the church and school which they operated, which was also funded by the same anonymous foundation as our clinic, was doing great. The forty-mile trip and time for visiting would take most of the day.

Before leaving, a knock at the door interrupted our thoughts. Anna went to answer the knock.

"Hello Boaz," I heard her say. "What brings you here this morning?"

"Hello, Miss Anna," Boaz said as he bowed politely. "Is Mr. Camel Doctor here?"

I stepped outside to greet my friend Boaz and to ask what he needed.

"Mr. Camel Doctor, I need you to go to my house and see about one of my camels," he requested.

"What's wrong with your camel, Boaz?" I asked.

"Well, he is not all that sick, but he won't get up when I command him to rise," explained Boaz. "He is my oldest and most obedient camel."

I tried to ease his mind. "Boaz, I remember when I visited with you one time that we could not get one of your camels to lie down," I chuckled. "Now this one won't get up!"

"This is the same camel. He sure has his 'ups and downs' but he is an old, old camel," he answered.

I told Anna that I was sorry to cancel our little outing but Boaz had a camel in real trouble. She assured me that she understood and that we could visit our friends later.

When we reached Boaz' house, he showed me that even though the old camel tried to obey his master's command to get up, he just couldn't seem to make it. I walked around the trusted camel and then I noticed his problem. The bottom of his left hind leg was positioned in a ninety degree angle from the top. I knew we had trouble! By feeling this leg, I noticed the bone, tendons and musculature of the limb were badly severed.

The old camel had a broken leg! His 2,000 pounds of weight and the brittleness of his aging bones added to the complications. The prognosis for his recovery was "nil," absolutely impossible. Knowing that Boaz held the camel as a "sacred animal," given to a man as a blessing to himself, his wife and family, I wondered how I would tell Boaz that his trusted camel would have to be put to sleep.,

"Boaz," I said reverently, "his leg is broken so badly that I can't do any helpful thing for him. The camel is so old that healing will never be possible."

I did not know what to expect. Boaz said, "Will you put my camel to sleep for me?" I was shocked! Did I hear his question correctly? The look in his eyes told me he understood.

"Yes I will, Boaz," I answered.,

I put the camel to sleep with the proper Euthanasia drug. The lame camel went to sleep slowly as I saw Boaz go into a small building and close the door. After I finished, I went to the door of the building and found Boaz quietly working with the last piece of camel leather he had.

"I didn't know you had a cobbler shop at home," I told him, noticing that he was making a beautiful pair of shoes.

"I have always made shoes any place when camel leather is available," he told me, "and it looks as though my leather supply has increased today! I am so glad that the Lord has taught me that it is good to use the things He gives us. The camel is given to ride, to carry our loads, to make coats and rugs, and to make leather shoes," he concluded.

I went back to the clinic where I found some work to do, but first I bowed my head and thanked the Lord for His help in my trip to see the camel.

Who is the Misfit?

Anna and I often thought about the future of the Fringe country. We had lived here for nearly two decades and we have seen some little changes occasionally, but they were few and far between. On the other hand, in some areas of Ethiopia, there were extreme differences.

Our little group of four, Sal, the agricultural agent; Ling, my veterinarian assistant; Anna and I met at our house to discuss the needs and the future of the Fringe country. We saw the coming infringement of the Communists growing closer, even though there was no natural wealth, or no industrial or commercial growth in sight at the time. To the north of us, the desert lands have nothing to offer except unconfirmed reports of salt deposits. We had been told that the salt deposits would be too expensive to mine and would not be competitive with other known sources. Some outsiders had even said that the Fringe country was a misfit in all of Africa.

I remembered hearing Miss Bessie tell about her early childhood days when her family moved from a "big stone mountain" in Georgia to her new home in Alabama. The area in Georgia, where her family had lived for many years was a rich, fertile farming community, and most of her family kindred lived nearby. The land had been abused with one cotton crop after another, until all the nutrients had been bleached from the soil.

Most of her family moved to the west in a wagon train around 1890. They were looking for more fertile soil and better grassland for their cattle. They traveled more than 160 miles before they found what they wanted. The wagon train was so heavily loaded, the young people in the family were not permitted to ride at all. They had to walk beside the mule-pulled wagons for nearly twenty-five miles every day.

As a small girl, Miss Bessie told of walking beside the wagons and often her father had to jump down from the wagon and drive the mules from a walking position. This was especially true on steep hills, because the wagons were so heavily loaded. When they came to a mountainous area in Alabama, called "Sand Mountain," they settled there and quickly learned the art of contour farming, with terraces separating the rows to preserve the soil.

Miss Bessie and her family are still on that same farm they settled in 1890. It is the same farm where Anna's father was killed when she was only eight years old. He was driving a team of horses while pulling a wagon loaded with loose hay. The horses became frightened and began running down a steep, winding hill, when her father fell between the traces of the horses and was caught by a single-tree hook, dragging him to his death. Miss Bessie never remarried, but continued to run the farm profitably for many years. Progress moved her family to another state and they may have been called misfits for awhile.

In the Fringe country, our little group realized that it was possible that a similar move may have to be made within the next several years. We were situated on the edge of two large plateaus which were gradually being swept away by the wind currents every day, making the area vulnerable to arid conditions.

Sal had to make a trip to the nation's capitol, Addis Ababa. We thought it might be good for me to go with him to observe the changes in the country. The three-hundred mile trip into the heartland, where eighty percent of Ethiopia's people live, would be hard and treacherous.

When I kissed Anna "goodbye," she began crying.

"Why are you crying?" I asked.

"I have some fear about what you are going to find during this trip," she replied. "I fear for you and Sal in that area where this is so much Communist activity."

"Don't worry," I told her, even though I felt kinda good about her loving me so much that it brought tears to her eyes.

Sal and I planned our trip to go through the farming area. The two large plateaus to our west had several small villages situated on the plains and surrounded by rugged mountains. Most of this area had an ideal climate, rich soil and ample rainfall to yield a potential rich agricultural harvest. The chief crops were millet, corn and cotton. There were also two crops for medical use: the narcotic "Kat," used for medical tonic and a castor bean which was used as medicine. Small amounts of coffee were grown in little patches where the farmer could only use a hoe for cultivation. We were told that the greatest area for producing coffee in this country was in the province of Jama, where it was their chief export.

In other places, the plow was used by most farmers for flatland farming. The villages were actually "wide places in the road," where round and square mud covered houses had a hemp-looking, tightly woven plant for their roofs. A few houses had a flat metal roof. The floors were mostly dirt, but some had beautiful, multi-colored wool rugs over the dirt floors.

The roads in this area followed the contour of the hills and creeks. They were crooked, narrow and dirt-based, with a few gravel in selected steep, tight places.

Sal and I noticed that the people in the areas, especially as we came nearer to Addis Ababa, were very suspicious of outsiders. There was an increasing, on-the-spot domination by the military. Frustration was everywhere! The people didn't know whether to trust us or not, fearing we, too, may be communists.

At Addis Ababa, we noticed a totally different atmosphere to that of the Fringe country. In the inner city, there were many modern buildings with beautiful streets with wide sidewalks lined with Eucalyptus trees. In any direction one might look there were large industrial buildings and factories. All of this was so different.

This well-developed city in the middle of a very poor and undeveloped country seemed out of place. It just didn't seem to fit in what we knew most about Ethiopia, but which was the misfit? The countryside or the city?

The military were everywhere! Most of the civilian businesses and offices were staffed by the military. While the city seemed to be prospering, Sal and I knew that it was at the expense of their outside countrymen. Also, we found out that this area was helped by the United States through the World Bank which gave thirty million dollars annually for the needs of the people of this country. The Communist Bloc nations, however, gave one hundred million dollars annually, which was used and distributed by the military. Very few dollars went to help the heartland farming people and almost nothing to the Fringe country.

When we returned home, Ling and Anna asked us many questions about the conditions of the heartland. We told them about seeing some of the public schools and even found some universities in the capitol city. There was some freedom of religion in the area, but not as many churches as we had expected. In the Fringe country, however, there were no public schools. But there was freedom of religion and several missionary schools were scattered among the people.

When comparing the crowds and activity of the nation's capitol and the surrounding heartland, with our slow-moving people of the Fringe country, which is the misfit?

Missionaries Go Home!

A full-days work was ahead of me. Mr. Salamon asked me to "worm" thirty of his sheep and that will take all day. At one time, the job could have been done easily and quickly, but the sheep had become "Americanized" and were afraid to be caught. They knew that the vet was going to hold them down while he treated them and vaccinated them. No wonder they ran when we came close to them, much like the ones on Miss Bessie's farm, eight thousand miles away.

When I finally returned to the clinic later in the day, Ling met me in the yard, excited almost to tears.

"Dr. Bill," he began. "Today an army vehicle stopped at the big tree down the road and tacked up a sign. Then they drove here to the clinic and gave me a sealed letter addressed to you!"

I opened the letter immediately and read:

NOTICE

All non-natives of this country, foreign missionaries or foreign Christ School missionaries, must depart from this country within ten (10) days of this notice.

Signed: Ethiopian Military Command

Date: 6 - 1 - 1972

"But Ling," I said. "I'm a veterinarian. This doesn't mean me!"

We went to the tree down the road to read the poster that had been placed there by the soldier. It read that all Christian missionaries must leave this area by June 10, 1972.

I went to tell Anna the news. She was very disturbed because she had come to love the Fringe country during the twenty-three years we had lived there. We told Sal about the notice and he also was very disturbed. He said he was going to see what he could do about the matter and left immediately. Why would they do this to us? Anna and I are not Bible-carrying missionaries, even though we are veterinarian missionaries. This is our home. We don't want to leave this place!

We learned the next day that our missionary friends near Barter Store III were not going to fight the new law. They had made up their minds that they would just go back to America.

Sal came to the clinic early the next morning and told us that he had learned the reason for the new law. He said the missionaries had suggested that public schools be built over the entire country and not just in Addis Ababa, the capital city.

The government, which was run by the military, decided to expel all missionaries, so they wouldn't have to bother with their suggestions. It was much easier to just tell the missionaries to go home!

"I'm going to Addis Ababa tomorrow," Sal told us. "I am going to tell them that Dr. William J. Isabell is not involved in this problem and that he should be able to stay here as a veterinarian."

"That's great, Sal," I replied. "We'll stay here and wait for your return. In the meanwhile, we will be thinking about some other plans too."

Within a couple of days, Sal returned from the long trip. "You're supposed to appear in an 'adjutant court' on October 9, 1972 at 8 A.M." he told me. He also gave me the name of the building and the room number where I was to appear.

"Don't worry," he assured me. "I'll be by your side, as a native man, to lend support."

When we reported in Addis Ababa, we were told by the court clerk that the judge was out of the country for the next five days. Until he returned, we would be placed under "house arrest" in a designated building. We would have nothing to do and no way to get in touch with Anna. The only thing I could do was to write a letter, which I did that afternoon.

The day for my appearance before the judge finally arrived. Sal, a native Ethiopian, would act in my defense. After the preliminaries were over, I was called before the judge.

"What do you have to say?" he asked me point-blank.

Before I had a chance to answer, there was a knock on the court room door. A man, wearing a turban, came into the room and approached the judge's bench.

"I am here to stand up with my Brother," he told the Judge as he moved toward me. He took the turban from his head and I noticed he was my friend Boaz.

"Mr. Judge," he began. "Why do you have my Brother here?"

"Who are you? Please identify yourself before this court," the Judge said.

"I am Boaz from the Fringe country, a camel owner and a man of the desert," Boaz replied. "You know how we 'nomads' take care of the desert for this country and how our country depends on us as honorable citizens."

"Yes," the Judge replied. "We all appreciate the camel people in our country. But, how do I know you are one of the camel people?"

Boaz walked to the window at the side of the courtyard. "These are my people who came here to Addis Ababa with me. And there is my camel," he said as he pointed out the window.

"Well, I can believe that you are a camel owner and those are your people," the Judge said. "But, how can I know that this light-skinned man that you stand with is your Brother? His skin is not that dark."

I whispered a quick prayer to the Lord. *Dear Lord, help Boaz with the right answer.*

Boaz threw me the turban he was holding in his hand. "He wears this all the time, not me! I just brought it to him," Boaz replied.

I placed the turban on my head as the Judge watched carefully.

"Well, well," the Judge finally said. "I believe you are right. He is your Brother and I can tell because he is wearing your turban."

The case was dismissed and the Judge said Anna and I could stay in the Fringe country as long as we lived.

I hugged Boaz before Sal and I left for home in the Jeep. The next day after arriving home, Anna got the letter I mailed from Addis Ababa. Three days later, Boaz and his friends arrived back at their homes since they had traveled the entire distance by slow-moving camels.

Chapter Eight

Twenty Minutes 'Til Half-Time

The Best Lawyer — The Best Verdict

TEN DAYS after my trial with the "Adjutant Court Judge" in Addis Ababa, I received an official order from the Judge declaring me a citizen of the country.

I had seen Boaz several times since returning from his long journey to the Capitol but I didn't really know how to thank him. The people of the Fringe country consider it an insult to be offered money for their good deeds. So, I went to his shop to order a pair of camel leather boots. Even though I have never liked boots which extended too high over my ankles, I decided that I would let Boaz make me some and pay him well for them.

As it was my day off from the clinic, I told Anna my plans to see Boaz. I put my hands on each of her shoulders and pulled her toward me in a gentle, loving bundle as I told her goodbye before leaving for the the cobbler shop. Then, I went by the clinic to tell Dr. Ling that I would be with Boaz, if he should need me.

"Hello, Boaz," I greeted him.

"Good morning, Brother Bill," he replied. "What can I do for you?"

I noticed that this was the first time Boaz ever called me by my first name. It had always been "Mr. Camel Doctor." But, he sensed that this was not camel business today.

"Boaz, I would like for you to make me a pair of high-top camel-leather boots," I began. "I've never really liked boots very tall. But, this time I want them tall with lots of pretty camel leather holding them together."

"I can do that for you," Boaz replied.

Boaz told me to sit down and remove my right shoe. He pulled my sock up tightly, yet in the normal position. I was surprised with his knowledge of the anatomy of the foot as he began to measure me.

"The bones of the foot form three arches, two running lengthwise and one running across the instep," he explained. He then placed a white sheet of paper under my foot and made an outline of my foot. He measured from arch to toe, and then to the heel.

Next, he recorded the width of my foot ten times in equidistance markings from the tip of the toe to the ball of the heel. The ankle measurements were also recorded. The calf of the leg was recorded in circumference in equidistance from the top of the boot, down to the ankle's medial extremities. All was measured and completed with each foot being recorded separately. He told me my boots would be finished in ten days.

"Thank you for measuring and mapping these boots so well," I told Boaz. "I also want to thank you for coming to my Adjutant Court trial. You did a wonderful thing for me and I appreciate it very much."

Boaz smiled. It was the biggest grin I had ever noticed in the many years I had known him. I sensed that he wanted to tell me something about the trial and its circumstances.

"You certainly timed your appearance at the trial just perfect," I told him. I knew that the slow moving camels had taken several days to make the long journey.

"My kindred live as nomads in the desert oasis north of us," Boaz began. "They are good people and are known as the 'good Samaritans' of the desert. Once every year, the government from Addis Ababa sends an Adjutant Judge to the oasis for their annual inspection. When I first heard about the date for your trial, I had my kindred to ask specifically for the judge that was to hear your trial to come for their inspection.

"I knew it would take several days to get to the heartland on my camels, so I had to delay the trial by getting the judge out of the city," he explained.

"You mean those five days Sal and I were kept in house arrest was really a defense maneuver directed by you? I asked.

"You make me sound like a lawyer, but that's about the verdict," Boaz laughed.

I pondered these things in my heart. For several moments I could not think about what to reply. The only thing I could think of came from the depths of my heart. "Boaz," I said reverently, "You sure are your brother's keeper."

I lingered at the cobbler's shop while watching Boaz work with the intricate measurements for the boots I had ordered. Again, I sensed that he wanted to tell me something more.

"Let me tell you something about my kindred who live in the north oasis of the desert," he began. "There was a man who was traveling from one town to another and while on his way, some thieves beat him and took all his money. He was left bleeding and unconscious on the side of the road.

"A little while later, a priest came along the road, and seeing the bleeding man, he passed by on the other side. Later, a Levite came by the wounded man and he too crossed to the other side of the road. But then, a Samaritan came along the same road and when he saw the half-dead man, he had compassion on him. He treated his wounds with wine and oil and then lifted him to his own beast and brought him to an inn.

"The next morning, the Samaritan told the innkeeper that he must continue on with his journey. But he left two pieces of silver with the innkeeper to pay for the wounded man's needs. He also told him that when he returned from his trip that he would pay any other expenses which were incurred for the wounded man," Boaz concluded.

We sat in silence for a few minutes. Then Boaz spoke again. "Thank you for listening to this story because the 'good Samaritan' in my story was my kinsman, and many of them still live in the north oasis of this desert."

"I like that story Boaz," I replied. "I must go now. But thank you for the new boots you are going to make for me and also thank you for being that 'good Samaritan.'"

We Make Camels Here

By the late 1970s, travel from Ethiopia to the U.S. had become less complicated. Anna and I could board a big British jet plane in Addis Ababa, and with only a few stops enroute, be whisked away to our destination in Alabama. Our two-month furloughs every two years always began at Miss Bessie's farm, where I continued to be known as the son-in-law who had taken her daughter away from her, some eight thousand miles away!

Anna always told her mother that the Fringe country was the best place in the world to live.Yet, Miss Bessie continued to operate the family farm and to encourage us to "come back home."

"Miss Bessie," I repeatedly told her, "We have committed at least another five years to the Trust Foundation. We must stay on the job at least another five years."

Miss Bessie always responded by throwing her hands up in the air in disgust. "What am I going to do with you children?" she would say. "If you wait for another five years, most of the farms around this area will be swallowed up in housing subdivisions, factories and office buildings."

It seemed hard to believe. How could this whole farm area become so populated that farming would cease? Yet, I found a clue to her thinking a few days later.

I had planned to visit Dr. Mac in Tennessee for a few days during our furlough. We always enjoy working together and catching up on the latest veterinary techniques. Anna planned to stay with her Mother while I made the eight hour trip to Dr. Mac's.

Each time I came to one of the many small towns in both Alabama and Tennessee, I noticed a traffic snarl. Large industrial plants and offices in practically every little town had seemed to appear from nowhere since my last trip home. Lines of slow moving automobiles and trucks congested the crowded highways. After several hours driving, I realized that I would not make it to Dr. Mac's house at a decent hour. I began looking for a motel to spend the night. There were several beautiful motels, with swimming pools, restaurants, and well-kept lawns. After stopping at each of them, the answer was always the same: "Sorry, we have no vacancies!" My, how things had changed since I was last home!

I finally had to stay at a rooming house, the only available place in the whole town. It was nearly 1 A.M. when I finally got to bed. I was glad Anna did not come with me. The traffic and lack of accommodations would have made her sick.

Early the next morning, I continued on my journey. The traffic was still heavy, at least by my standards, and I noticed several industrialized areas along the way. There were factories, warehouses for cotton textiles, furniture making, tobacco loose-leaf and re-dry plants, with bellowing clouds of stream flowing upward into the sky.

As I was nearing one large city, a huge billboard attracted my attention. Attached to the roof of a large building, the sign had a picture of my favorite animal, the camel. Under the camel was the caption, "I'd Walk a Mile for a Camel!" How did my beloved camel get here in the U.S. where its population is zero? Being away from my country for so long, I just didn't understand. There must be some explanation.

I parked my car in an adjacent parking lot and entered the building. There was a long line of people just inside the door and I waited my turn to speak to the receptionist. When I finally reached the desk I noticed that each person ahead of me was given an application to complete.

"Can I ask you one question?" I said to the receptionist.

"Surely," she said, as she looked up.

"What kind of a factory is this?" I asked.

"We make camels here," was her reply.

I learned that the building was a cigarette factory where they made a specific brand of popular cigarettes — Camels, and that the people in front of me were competing to be on a radio talk show sponsored by the Camel Cigarette Company.

"Where do you live? the receptionist asked me.

"I live in Eastern Africa and am home for a couple of months on furlough."

"Well, I'm sorry that we cannot use you on our radio program," she began. "Our policy is to use only people here in the U.S. What kind of work do you do in Africa?"

95

"I'm a veterinarian, a camel specialist in Ethiopia,"

She looked questionably at me for a moment and then asked if I would be seated until she got her boss. In a few moments, she returned with her boss who seemed to be very excited.

"This is the opportunity of a lifetime," he told me. "Just think, we can have a real camel specialist on our radio program. Just wait until I tell those guys in New York what I have found. They'll never believe it!" he went on.

We talked for a little while and I was told that the company would fly Anna and me back to the U.S. in about six months, with all expenses paid! I accepted their offer contingent on Anna's agreement.

I went on to Dr. Mac's clinic and practiced for a few days doing large animal work. Three days later, I returned home and told Anna about the offer by the Camel people. She was excited about the radio program and the opportunity to have an all expense paid trip to New York. I told Miss Bessie about the severe traffic problems on the way to Dr. Mac's house.

"Now you see what I mean when I told you that these farms around here may be lost to industry," she said. "Already, many choice farms are being cut apart by new interstate highways and businesses everywhere."

Anna's Secret

It was the middle of March and we were scheduled for our furlough during the summer. I had noticed that there had been regular correspondence between Anna and Miss Bessie for several months and most of them had been marked "personal" in Miss Bessie's own handwriting. When I asked Anna about this great mystery, she just smiled and told me it was a secret. This was not like Anna, to keep anything secret from me. We had always shared our deepest thoughts with each other. What was going on?

Anna suggested that we postpone our furlough until November and December, in order to be home for Christmas. I thought it was an excellent idea. We had not been home for the holidays in our thirty years in Africa.

We arrived at Miss Bessie's farm in mid-November and went straight to our old house next to Miss Bessie's. Anna seemed to want to wait for her Mother to come over to see us. Usually, we went to her house first.

When Miss Bessie arrived, Anna took me by the hand and led me to her Mother's car. She started the motor and headed up the road to a beautiful area of thick pine trees. We turned into a newly built road and followed the lane until we saw a beautiful, newly built brick ranch-type house, with a freshly seeded lawn surrounding it.

"Anna and Bill," Miss Bessie said. "This is your new home!"

"You can't mean it," I gasped.

"Oh yes," Anna said joyfully. "This was the secret between Mother and me for the past several months. We wanted to surprise you."

"Well, you certainly did," I said as I leaped out of the car and made my way to the front door. I couldn't believe it! We went inside and the house was so beautiful and spacious.

"This is why your trip was delayed this year, Bill," Miss Bessie said. "The house was not quite finished and we needed more time. As a matter of fact, the brick on the back wall is still not finished, but we expect the bricks to be here in a few days."

Both Anna and I thanked Miss Bessie over and over. We were still feeling the effects of jet-lag, but our joy was overwhelming. We went back to our old house for a night's rest.

The next day, we moved our furniture from the old house into our new home. We stopped periodically to admire the roominess of our new house.

Early the following morning, I was awakened by the roar of the engine of a large truck at the rear of our house. The heavy fog had caused the driver to miss the driveway and the big truck, even though only half loaded, had sunk the rear tires in the fresh mud. Despite all his efforts, the driver could not get the truck to move.

"What can we do?" I asked the driver. "Can I help in any way?"

The driver got out of the truck and very calmly surveyed the situation. Then he told me that all the weight was on the two back wheels of the truck. He explained that the weight would have to be shifted so that it was over the axle that pulls the truck. He manipulated the hydraulic crane and in a few seconds had moved the entire load of bricks to the front of the truck. The calm driver got back into the truck and started the motor. Sure enough, the truck moved and he was again on a solid foundation.

After the bricks were unloaded, I asked, "What ever made you think about moving the bricks to the front of the truck?"

"I need to tell you something," he began. "You asked me how I knew to rotate my load to the front of the truck for better traction. Well, I don't know if you go to church or not, but I go everytime the doors are open. I just want you to know that the Good Lord must have helped me, because when I saw the problem, the answer came to me so quickly, it must have been from the Lord," he concluded.

I listened as the sound of the big truck grew fainter as it went out of hearing distance. When all was quiet, I thought, "I wish Miss Bessie could have heard the truck driver give his testimony. She probably would have said, 'Amen.'"

The Camel's Christmas List

Church on Christmas day! Our first Christmas home in thirty years and the holiday was celebrated on Sunday. Miss Bessie had asked me to have a part in the children's story time. The children were still at the age when Christmas was so exciting and the belief in Santa Claus mystified all of them. They still believed in the reindeer, North Pole, and that Santa opens and responds to every letter written to him by believing children.

I arrived at the church ahead of time and prepared the show-and-tell poster of my beloved camel at the front of the sanctuary and placed a neat white cloth over the poster. When the children were called to the front of the sanctuary, they stood in rapt attention, wondering what was under the white cloth.

"Merry Christmas to all of you children," I began. "I am so glad that you are here." I paused for a second then I asked, "How many of you wrote a letter to Santa Claus?"

Nearly all of the boys and girls raised their hands high in the air as they looked at one another.

"Well, can you tell me what you asked Santa to bring you for Christmas?"

There was a clamor of voices and I heard such answers as a doll, a wagon, a cowboy suit, a doll buggy, a train set, and the list went on.

"I brought an old friend of mine with me today, all the way from Africa. I want to tell you how he observes Christmas," I told the children while unveiling the picture. The old camel's face seemed to look them squarely in the eyes. His big eyelids were opened slightly and he seemed to be looking at each child individually.

"How many of you know what kind of animal this is?" I asked.

"A camel," they cried, almost in unison.

"Boys and girls, if you look at the animal very closely, you will notice that he is not the prettiest animal in the world. His head is too small for his large body, his legs are too long, and the hump on his back seems to be out of place. You will agree that he is a very funny looking animal indeed.

"One day, this old camel became worried about his funny looks and he decided to write to Santa Claus to see if he could get some of these funny looking things changed. In his letter he said,

Dear Santa,

Please send me some new legs that are a little shorter, maybe about the length of a cow. Please send me a back that is straight without a hump. Please send me a larger head, more like the size of a horse and please send me a shorter neck, about the length of a sheep.

Then the old camel signed his name, put a stamp on the envelope and mailed it to the North Pole.

"For several days, the old camel thought about how pretty he was going to be on Christmas day. He began to think about what he could do with his new appearance and his new look. He would have an entirely new life with all of these fine features.

"As he continued to think about his new look, he suddenly realized that he would lose his job. You see children, when the star first appeared over Bethlehem, the wise men needed to make the long trip across desert sands to see the Christ child in the manger. No other animal would be able to cross the waterless desert, except the camel. If he no longer had the funny looking hump on his back, he would not have a place to store water for the long trip. If he had shorter legs, he would not be able to walk so easily across the deep sand.

"The old camel quickly wrote to Santa again.

Dear Santa,

Please cancel all the things I asked for in my letter. I want to stay just like I am so I will be able to carry the wise men to see the Christ child in Bethlehem.

"Boys and girls," I concluded. "You are very special and no one else is exactly like you. You may wish you could change your image but you were created by God to be just like you are. We must be thankful that we are healthy and strong and that we can do all those things that the Lord wants us to do for our happiness. We must be happy for the gifts we give and receive, but we should be most happy because we know that Christ was born as a gift to all of us."

Half Time

One day, after returning from our Christmas furlough, I had scheduled a four-mile trip to treat an infected cow. When I went to get into the Jeep, I noticed that it had a flat tire and there was not a spare available at the time.

The cow's owner had given me a thorough description of the cow's sickness, so I determined to walk the four miles to his farm and take my Boston bag along with me. My practice bag is not too heavy and it contains most of the things I'd need. By the time I had walked two miles, I had become tired and the hot sun reminded me that I needed to stop and rest for a while.

Even though I did not consider myself very old, I still was not conditioned for walking four miles at one time. I sat down for a few minutes and then resumed my walk to the farm where I was needed. A woman met me at the door and said her husband had gone to the millet mill, but that he would be back about noon. I assured her I would treat the cow and leave her instruction for future treatments.

When I got to the stable, I noticed the cow was standing in a prancing, restless motion, with her rear limbs extending outward. Her udder was swollen, red and hot to the touch. I immediately recognized mastitis in one half of her udder. This meant that the thick, infected, clotted milk must be stripped from her three times a day. I would need to inject some antibiotics through the teat canal to reach the inflamed, inside walls of the udder. Then, I must bathe the outside of the udder with medicated Vaseline for treatment and protection.

After giving my instructions to the farmer's wife, I began my four-mile trip back home. I thought about that cow, who was probably mid-way in her productive years as a milk cow. Half of her udder was involved. With the proper treatment she would be a good milk producer for the remaining one-half of her life.

While resting half-way on my trip back home. I thought that it would be good for everyone to have an intermission, a half-time in their life to re-think their direction. I remembered the young man, who was probably half-way in his life, who came to Jesus one day and asked what he must do to inherit eternal life. He apparently had all the world had to offer, yet, he lacked the most important — the real meaning of life.

Our entire Bible has more than 25,000 verses, and along the way this man stopped to ask a definition of life. All that was written before this question, and all that is written afterwards, lends needful definition and clarity to life. This intermission or half-time commitment teaches us that eternal life begins when we stop any place along the way and commit our lives to Him.

Half-time intermissions also purge us of infection that may destroy us, and the beauty that the Lord intended for each of our lives. Sitting by the side of the road, I thought that perhaps this was my intermission, the half-time in my life. I did not see any great achievements or high marks in my life, but I was grateful that the Lord had made some lasting marks on my heart and that is why I am telling this story.

Chapter Nine

Second Half

Best Bull Is Ignored

LOOKING BACK over the years we spent in the Fringe country, I can see many definite areas of improvement. The clinic served many hundreds of people around Barter Store I and we had made many, many friends in Ethiopia.

Anna and I became in a real sense, people of two continents. On each continent we had one particular, precious person who proved to be constant companions in our unique work. In America, there was Miss Bessie, my mother-in-law, who for forty years continued to operate her farm and saw to it that our needs, both at home and abroad, were met. In Africa, there was Boaz, known as the "good Samaritan," who showed sincere compassion to us from the very beginning. What more could we have asked for when we began the second half of our lives?

Our ministry was blessed with great achievements in many ways. Sal, my old schoolmate and the one who had invited me to work in his homeland, applied his education as an agriculturalist, making the millet fields almost double in production in the last twenty years. His improved variety, fertilization and cultivation methods added greatly to the lives of his people. The animal programs also greatly improved. Through care and selective breeding, the milk production increased beyond our expectations.

I remember one day when Sal and I talked about the dairy herds. We had noticed that among the farmers who were fortunate enough to have a good breeding bull, there was an increase in milk production. Many farmers, however, had only one cow and could not afford a bull for reproduction, nor could they expect to have an increase in milk production in the future.

Sal and I studied artificial insemination which was being practiced in the United States. There, the large dairy associations were organized and used only the best breeding studs. Because of this, milk production was greatly increased. A breeding technician would go from farm to farm, impregnating the cows. This always resulted in increased production.

We agreed that such artificial insemination would be beneficial for the farmers in the Fringe country. But, where could we find a choice bull for our project? Surely the anonymous trust fund in the U.S. would help us to secure one. After all, I had been given the authority to write a check for any investment needed in our clinical work to help the people.

Sal and I made a trip to the best farming area in all Ethiopia. Our journey took us into the heartland, toward Addis Ababa, where most of the large farms were controlled by the government. They had the best bulls in the country, so we might be able to find what we wanted there. While studying at the University, Sal had investigated many types and breeds of bulls and had narrowed the choice to one specific breed.

After a thorough search, we arrived at one of the best farms in all of Ethiopia. There were many choice bulls at the farm and we were told that we could buy one for use in the Fringe country.

"I have many good bulls," the herdsman told us. "I'll go down the line and point out their superior qualities."

We noticed the salesman telling us about this bull and then the next. Sal spotted the bull he thought we really wanted in a separate pen. The herdsman completely ignored the bull of our choice.

Finally, Sal asked, "What about this bull?"

"He is the best bull we have. I don't think you would be interested in that one," the salesman replied. "There is no way you would be able to afford his price."

"What is the price?" Sal asked.

"That bull is worth $40,000!" we were told.

Sal and I quickly stepped aside to discuss the situation. I wanted to know if Sal really thought this bull was the best and was it really worth that much money.

"Yes, " Sal told me. "If we had that kind of money, the bull is definitely worth the price. It is probably the best bull in all of Ethiopia," he announced.

What shall I do? How could I make such a big decision? Finally, I whispered a prayer: *Lord, I need Your help to make this big decision. Please show me what to do!*

"We'll take this bull," I told the astonished salesman, "and I will make full payment to you today." I made out the blank check in the proper fashion from the "Fringe Country American Anonymous Trust Fund."

As soon as we got back to the clinic, I notified the Trust Foundation about the large check I had written. I waited to hear their reaction. In a few days a letter came. It contained several things about the ministry and some of the plans we had informed them about. At the end of the letter was a post script: "We are happy with the purchase of the new bull. We hope you spent ample time searching for the right bull, however, because we intend for you and the Fringe country to have the best in the land."

I was greatly relieved. The letter touched me deeply and I appreciated the confidence they had shown in me.

Lemac — Camel

The time arrived for our all-expenses-paid trip to New York to appear on the Camel Cigarette Radio Show. Anna and I were flown from Africa to New York. We were put up in a beautiful hotel near Radio City. When we checked in we were told that a prize could also be won if we could identify several animals beginning with the letters L-E-M-A-C, which is Camel spelled backwards.

The next day as we made our appearance on the show the announcer said, "Our next contestants are from the continent of Africa. What are your names?"

"My name is Dr. William J. Isabell and this is my wife Anna," I replied.

"Let's welcome Bill and Anna," the announcer told the audience and then there was a roaring applause. "Bill, tell us about your occupation."

"I am a veterinarian," I quickly responded.

"Do you have a particular specialization?" he asked.

"I am a camel specialist," I told him and there was another outburst of enthusiastic applause.

"Tell us Bill. Did you ride your camel to the show today?"

"No, not today," I answered.

"Why didn't you ride your camel today?" he joked.

"Well, my camel is known as the 'ship of the desert,'" I told the audience, "but not the 'ship of the ocean.' I don't believe he could swim that far." I hesitated a moment. "But, he might be able to swim that far. I just haven't tried him yet!"

The audience laughed.

"It's a pleasure to talk with you but let's get on with the show," the announcer said. "You understand the way we play our little game. If you answer all the questions correctly, spelling the word LEMAC, you win a prize. Your category is animal questions.

"The first question is to identify an animal, beginning with the letter L. What is the animal with a roaring voice?"

Anna replied quickly, "A lion."

"That's right," the announcer said. "Next, what is the animal with a big trunk and snout, beginning with the letter E?"

"It's an elephant," Anna again answered.

"Good! Now for the third question. What is the small animal that is caught in a trap?" the announcer asked.

"That's easy," Anna said. "It's a mouse."

"You're right again. Now for the next question. What is the animal which has a body encased in an armor of small bony plates, and begins with the letter A?" he asked.

Anna was quick again and answered, "The armadillo."

"Wonderful," the announcer said. "Answer one more question correctly and you have spelled LEMAC. What is the animal that has a hump on his back, a head too small for its body, legs so long it must kneel down to have its cargo loaded, and has a cigarette named for him?"

I quickly interrupted Anna who was about to give the answer again. "Please Anna," I said. "I know this one. It is the camel!"

The audience applauded wildly while the band played their familiar theme song about the LEMAC — camel spelled backwards.

When we got home to the Fringe country from New York, I saw Boaz standing near his camel and went to tell him about the radio appearance. I told him that we had spelled camel backwards on the show and had won a prize.

"How much would they pay me to spell BOAZ backwards?" he joked. "ZAOB doesn't say much though," he laughed. Then he showed his unique sense of humor when he added, "Miss Anna could win everytime since it is the same backwards or forwards!"

Where Are My Grandchildren?

A few years after we were married, Anna asked me to sit down for a serious discussion. I could always tell when she had something really serious to talk about because she always asked me to be seated.

"Bill," she began. "Suppose you had a herd of cows and a healthy bull but they never produced any calves. What would you do?"

"Well, as a veterinarian, I would use a scientific medical examination to find out why there was no increase in the herd," I answered. I still did not know why she was asking such a question.

Then Anna got to the heart of her discussion. "I just don't know why the Lord has not blessed us with children. Most couples our age already have two or three children by this time."

I knew that Anna loved children very much. I used to watch her face brighten when helping the native children feed the little goats. She managed them so well, making them take turns during the feeding process. Everytime they visited, which was quite often, she gave them millet cookies and a glass of milk before leaving.

107

Even when on furlough in the States, she always loved to play with her young nieces and their dolls. She was elated even when playing baseball with the older children.

Anna continued our discussion. "I think both of us should arrange to have a complete physical examination the next time we are home on furlough. Then we can determine what our problem is medically."

I agreed fully with her reasoning. We would be on furlough in a few months and could talk about it with Miss Bessie.

When we arrived back in the United States, we went directly to our house and called Miss Bessie. She came over immediately and we talked for nearly an hour. Then Anna got really serious with her Mother.

"Mama," she began. "Bill and I have something to discuss with you. It is highly possible that you may say it is none of your business and that we should do whatever we think best. But, we have been thinking about a family of our own and don't understand why we do not have any children.

"We think we should get some medical advice or have a complete physical examination to determine what our problems are."

"Well kids, I have been thinking about this for sometime. I've wondered why you two haven't given me any grandchildren," Miss Bessie said. "I support you wholeheartedly in this and will be glad to supply the money for the examinations."

"Oh No!" I said quickly. "We are not coming to you for money. You are the best and most dependable family we have in America since my folks died. We just want your advice."

The next day, Anna and I went to our doctor. After complete examinations, both of us passed with flying colors. We were both extremely healthy. There was no specific problem with Anna, but in my childhood medical records, there was a problem which prevented me from being able to father children. The doctor told us that when I was a child I had a complicated case of mumps and this apparently was the reason.

As we drove back to Miss Bessie's, we were both disappointed. Miss Bessie could see the gloom on our faces and tried to cheer us. "Take heart, both of you," she

108

encouraged. "You still have each other and I have both of you," she said as she took both of us in her arms. "And remember! The good Lord is still in charge!"

Your Bottom as Tough as a Camel

Winter time in the Fringe country cannot be compared to the winters in the United States. There is a specific difference, however, in the wind and temperature. I remember getting a call one morning during the winter, to treat a heard of cows for "blackleg."

This is a common disease among calves under two years of age. The make-up of their muscle tissue makes them susceptible to blackleg. Usually, the disease is not as common in the winter months as it is in the dry, hot, short grass-picking time of the year.

Postmortem examination of the limbs of diseased calves show dark tissues and a gas formation in the muscles. There is no cure for blackleg. The only protection for the calves is a vaccination of a bacterium for immunization.

We rounded up the herd while a cold wind and howling rain beat upon our faces and drenched us thoroughly. After immunizing the calves, I went home, cold and soaked, with not a dry spot on my body. Three days later I was sick with a cold and my body ached all over. My temperature rose to 103°.

Anna called the Monastery near Barter Store II and asked for Dr. Ben Alex to come and see me. Later in the day, the doctor came and must have talked for an hour before getting around to examining me. We learned that he was from New York and had come to the Fringe country five years earlier as a missionary doctor.

I noticed that he was driving a new Jeep, much like the one I had for my veterinary practice.

"Let me ask you a personal question," I said to Dr. Alex. He nodded his approval. "I know that the people here do not have enough money to support you. How do you get enough money to keep up your practice?"

"The fact of the matter," Dr. Alex replied, "I don't know who supports me. All I know is that there is an anonymous Trust Foundation in the U.S. that seems to have a lot of money because they give me all I need for my medical clinic."

"Well, isn't that something," I added. "I also have an anonymous trust foundation in the U. S. that supports me. Do you think they may be the same people?"

Dr. Alex did not know the answer any more than I, so we did not pursue the mystery any further. He gave me a thorough examination and concluded that I had the "flu." He then commanded me to roll over on my stomach, raw bottom up in the position for a shot of penicillin. When his needle met the skin on my bottom, it came to an abrupt stop! He had a difficult time piercing through the tough skin.

"How many miles do you ride each year on this bottom of yours?" he asked. "Your rear is as tough as a camel's hide!"

Anna was standing in the doorway to the next room listening to the doctor. "I think my husband is part camel. Anyway, if he isn't, he sure would like to be!"

Four days later I was back on the road, making my bottom tougher than a camel's hide as I bounced along the rough roads.

Chapter Ten

My Devotion to Animals

Glad You Are at Home, Mr. Sandburg

MY BI-ANNUAL working trip to Dr. Mac's clinic in Tennessee always produced some interesting observations. It afforded me the opportunity to get caught up with the latest research while enjoying some days of nostalgia as well.

One of those days while on a furlough to the U.S. remains indelibly etched in my mind. We had had the usual number of vaccinations of dogs during the morning. A lull in the afternoon permitted us to get caught up on routine cleaning. The instruments had all been cleaned, disinfected and autoclaved. The display of drugs on the counter and the racks had all been dusted, with everything arranged and in their proper places.

Dr. Mac's clinic, one of the few in his area, had facilities for large animals, with stalls to keep the animals overnight. The stalls were always kept clean with fresh straw and each was well-lighted. Dutch-type doors were hinged so that the upper section could be opened separately and then fastened on a metal hook. The stalls, stables, and wide shed which was attached were always well groomed, ready for a Royal inspection or even Royal occupancy.

Near the end of the day, after the two clinic helpers had finished their work, Dr. Mac and I stayed for an additional hour before closing. A flat-bed farm truck with cattle racks pulled into the driveway and up to the chute area.

"Hello, Mr. Krisle," Dr. Mac called. "What's that you have in the back of your truck?"

"I have a young heifer calf with a broken leg," he replied.

Dr. Mac examined the calf and noticed it had a clean break in the shank bone of the right rear limb. It was the kind of break that usually makes for a good prognosis.

"We can put the calf in one of the stables," Dr. Mac said. "After supper, I can set its leg."

Before the truck had left, we saw a large, black, Cadillac limousine pull into the driveway. It was certainly one well-kept automobile — the kind that usually had a jump seat between the front and rear seats.

A tall middle-aged man wearing a black suit got out from the driver's side. As he approached us, he asked, "Are you the veterinarian?"

"Yes sir. I am," Dr. Mac replied.

"Mr. Sandburg would like to talk to you."

We went to the passenger side of the car where Mr. Sandburg was sitting. As we reached the car, we saw gray locks of flowing hair framing Mr. Sandburg's distinguished face. Dr. Mac immediately recognized that he was Mr. Carl Sandburg, the Pulitzer prize winner in two fields: history and poetry.

"We're glad you are still here," the renowned author said. "We hope you can keep two of our goats for the night."

"Yes sir, we will be glad to keep your goats for you," Mac answered.

"I see you're busy right now," the celebrity said. "Go ahead with your work and, if you don't mind, I'd like to watch you."

He came to the side of the truck and looked through the cattle racks at the calf with the broken leg. Then he walked alongside us as we put the injured animal into his clean stall. Mr. Krisle told us that he would be back in the morning to pick up his calf because it was dependent on its mother for nursing.

We sensed that Mr. Sandburg did not want his identity to be known for the present. Neither of us said anything about him. We just went back to his car to get the goats.

The jump seats in the center area of the rear floor had been removed and an attractive crate made of aluminum tubing was in their place. Two beautiful, prize winning, milk goats were standing side by side, waiting anxiously to get out of the crate as soon as the gate was opened. We led the goats by their new leather halters and reins to their appointed stable for the night.

"You have a very nice place here," Mr. Sandburg remarked. "Everything is so convenient and clean, with fresh straw in every stall."

Dr. Mac thanked him and allowed the celebrity to put his own special goat feed, which he had brought along with him from home, into the feeding bunkers.

"Doctor," Mr. Sandburg said softly. "You have such a great opportunity to help animals as a vet. I am almost jealous of you!" He looked around the stables and then back to his prize goats. "I guess we're finished here. The goats are fed and bedded down for the night. My driver is going to have the car serviced. As he'll be gone for a while, I would like to stay and help you set that break on the little Herefords leg."

"Oh no, Mr. Sandburg," Dr. Mac replied. "I can do that by myself a little later."

"But, I really want to help," the author insisted.

"Well, all right. We need to go to the dispensary room to get my supplies," Dr. Mac told him.

When they returned, the calf was slightly sedated for ease and stillness while they did their work. They placed the calf on a heavy table which was attached to the wall with hinges. Mr. Sandburg continued to ask questions about the cotton padding, Uka board splint materials, gauze, tape, and the plaster of Paris, which were used to make the multi-plied splint.

As they finished, the calf seemed to "shake off" the low dose sedative drug. Dr. Mac picked up the young calf with both arms and stood it on the clean straw in the center of the stall. Mr. Sandburg reached down and hugged the little calf with both arms, as he watched the young Hereford stand on the new crutch he had helped to make.

"I feel so good because I stayed to help you," Mr. Sandburg told Dr. Mac. "We were like two vets working on this case."

About that time, Mr. Sandburg's driver had returned from getting the car serviced. They drove off together to a nearby motel after thanking and assuring us that they would return in the morning.

Early the next morning, the black limousine pulled into the driveway. Mr. Sandburg went to see the little Hereford calf and to check on his splint. Then he fed his goats. While the goats were eating, we sat on the stable doorsill and talked about many things. The renowned author even sang a few lines of a new song he had written.

After we had placed his goats into the car, Mr. Sandburg rolled down his window. "I guess we're ready to go," he told Dr. Mac. "I want to thank you and tell you that I have enjoyed my visit with you. I need to know, however, what your charge is for keeping my goats overnight."

"Mr. Carl Sandburg," Dr. Mac addressed him. "You don't owe me anything. As a matter of fact, I feel like I owe you for winning the Pulitzer prize for history and poetry for our country.

The celebrated poet did not seem to know how to respond. It looked like he wanted to cry and smile at the same time. "Cut the motor off, Bob," he told his driver.

He got out of the car and walked with Dr. Mac to the stable once again. Kneeling down by the little calf he asked Dr. Mac what kind of treatment and care the young Hereford would need for the next few days.

"I wish I knew how to tell you what is in my heart right now," he told Dr. Mac. "I want to thank you again for allowing me to be 'the other vet' on this case. I feel like I have earned another award, better than the others, by finding a friend like you today."

Dr. Mac was deeply touched. As Mr. Sandburg's limousine went through the front gate and disappeared over the hill, Mac stood waving goodbye. He knew the celebrated author was on his way back to his farm, "Connemara," on the Eastern slopes of the Blue Ridge Mountains.

You may wonder why Mr. Carl Sandburg happened to stop at Dr. Mac's clinic with his milk goats this particular day in the early 60s. The clinic, in rural Tennessee, was located between the Ozark Mountains and the Blue Ridge Mountains where Mr. Sandburg lived. In the Ozarks he had bought two new goats for his herd and was returning home.

He had stopped along the Interstate and was told that the only place which had overnight accommodations for such animals was Dr. Mac's clinic, which was 35 miles out of his way.

Dr. Mac continued to communicate with Mr. Sandburg during the last years of his life. He always asked about the little calf whose leg he had helped to set. In each letter, he always invited Dr. Mac to "Connemara." Dr. Mac took him up on it and visited twice before Mr. Sandburg died in 1967.

Start My Day Twice

Even in the Fringe country, cows do not always time their illness to go along with normal office hours. Early one morning, long before daylight, I was awakened by a farmer who had a "milk fever cow" that required emergency treatment. The cow was very low, even near death, but the treatment for "milk fever" always works within about forty minutes after being administered. These quick results always did amaze me. In a short time, the cow was up and licking her new calf. My work was completed and the results were excellent.

On the way home as I passed Boaz' house, I noticed a dim light through the gray swirl clouds and thought I ought to stop to see him. I knew it was very early, but at least he seemed to be up and going about his business. And at that, I had not yet picked up the new boots I had ordered the month before.

"Good morning, Boaz," I said as I looked around his shop. There was something very different from the last time I had been here. "You sure are working early on this fine morning."

"Yes, I am;" he replied. "I need to get my new building finished before bad weather sets in."

I looked around the spacious new building. It covered more area than his entire house now. For this part of the world, it was a masterpiece.

"Let me show you around my new shop," Boaz offered. "This area is for shoe repair, this one for making new shoes," he continued as we walked and he pointed. "This space is for camel rugs and this is for camel coats."

"This is sure nice, Boaz. How did you get it done so quickly?" I asked.

115

"My people who live out in the desert at the 'Good Samaritan Oasis,' came and helped me."

"Well, I sure like your new building," I told him. "I guess, since I am here, I'll just pick up my new boots you have made for me."

Boaz looked sad and disappointed, then dropped his eyes toward the floor. "I'm sorry, Brother Bill, but I've been working day and night with this new store, and I haven't finished them yet."

"That's all right, Boaz," I said. "Don't worry a bit about that. Besides, I can't wear those boots for another two months when the cold weather sets in. I really don't need them now."

"I hope it is okay and I hope you like my new shop," Boaz apologized. "Someday I'll tell you why I built this shop. My business is going so well right now, that I have ten shoe cobblers working for me full-time."

I came home with mixed emotions. I felt badly about Boaz having to work so hard, yet glad that his business was doing so well. But, I wondered why he said that he would tell me later why he had built his new cobbler shop.

When I arrived home, it was nearly breakfast time. Anna had prepared omelets and millet patty cakes with sweet cane syrup and Jama coffee, grown nearby. It was the best coffee in the world!

After breakfast, I had a sudden urge to hold Anna. It seemed as though I loved her more at that moment than anytime in my life. We were so far from our families in the U.S., yet, she was all I could ever want and so much more. I held her tightly and told her goodbye as I made my way to the clinic to begin my day — for the second time!

The Camel Competes with the Automobile

The appearance on the Camel Radio Program had apparently gotten us some notoriety. I had received an invitation to be the guest speaker for the National Automobile Association. After the invitation arrived, I wondered why they would want a veterinarian, a camel specialist as a speaker. Was it because the camel is a mode of transportation? Was it because the camel is not in competition with the automobile, or because all the executives from the various companies wanted someone who would not cause dissention? Or, did they just want a "gimmick" speaker?

Anna and I arrived in New York the day before the convention. I had written a friend at the Camel Cigarette company to send me the largest picture of a camel he could find. Sure enough, when I asked at the reception desk of the hotel, there was a huge picture of a beautiful camel — and I certainly considered him to be beautiful — waiting for me.

During the recess before I was to speak, I taped the huge camel picture on the wall, directly behind the speakers podium. The automobile executives from the Big Three: Ford, General Motors, and Chrysler were there. Most of the smaller companies were also well represented. The convention hall was nearly filled when the moderator sounded his gavel. In a few minutes, I was introduced as a "Camel Specialist, all the way from Ethiopia, Africa." There was the customary round of applause as I walked to the speaker's stand.

"Thank you, Mr. Chairman," I began. "I want to thank you for inviting me and my camel to this automobile convention. Frankly, I don't know who was responsible for inviting me, but I do wonder if he really knew what he was doing." There was loud laughter across the convention hall.

"I might as well be fair with you from the very beginning. This camel, (I pointed to the poster behind me) is a fierce competitor to your automobiles. Now, I didn't ride a camel to this convention. The reason is obvious: the ocean is too wide between this continent and the continent of Africa.

"However, the camel is highly competitive to your cars and I will prove it. Your designers have copied so many features of my camel for your automobiles, I think you owe him some royalties. For instance, look at his eyes. You see that his eyelids are overhanding to protect them from the rain, sand, and sun. Some of you have adopted the same thing with your headlights and windshields. I think the old camel should collect a royalty." Again, there was a burst of laughter and some of the fellows applauded.

"Some of your cars and trucks now come equipped with heavy-duty shocks, which raises the back end up high. Well, the camel already has long legs, two times the length of a horse, and he can kneel to accept his cargo which is equal to that of one of your pick-up trucks. I think you fellows should give the camel another royalty.

"Furthermore, there are some areas where your cars and trucks cannot compete with the camel. Look at the hump on his back. Do any of your vehicles have a forty gallon capacity for gasoline? No! the maximum is usually only about twenty-five gallons. And, the camel can go on that fuel, eight hours a day, for several days, without running out. Can any of your cars do the same?

"I know that the old camel cannot travel quite as fast as your cars. As a matter of fact, his top speed is usually about two and one-half miles an hour. But, that is not all bad! Did you ever hear of anyone being hit by a speeding camel?" The audience roared.

"Well, I don't think you will have to worry too much as the camel as a competitor here in the U.S. Actually, the camel population here is zero. He belongs in the desert country and he is the oldest domesticated animal known to man.

"In biblical times of Job and Abraham, the camel was used exclusively. When Christ was born the wise men came to worship Him, aided by a bright star and a sure-footed camel. One day I asked a wise religious man if he thought my obsessive love for the camel was misdirected. He said, 'No. As long as there is a desert and a man, there must be a camel.'

"I doubt that I could sell many camels here in the U.S., but, you would have a hard time selling your automobiles in the desert country also. In the camel's desert, the sand is sometimes twelve feet deep and your automobiles would never make it there. So, I guess I would have to conclude that the camel and the automobile are not too competitive. But, I thank you for listening to me anyway!"

The meeting was adjourned with roars of laughter and thundering applause.

Chapter Eleven

Efforts to Recall

Father Had a Camel Store

IT HAD BEEN nearly two months since I last visited Boaz. Surely, he had finished working on his new store and by now had finished my boots. At least, I knew that I should go to see my good and trusted friend.

"Hello, Boaz," I greeted him. "I hope you have had time to work on my boots."

"Sure have, Brother Bill," he replied. "Let me go get them for you."

In a few moments he returned, smiling from ear to ear and holding the most beautiful boots I had ever seen. He handed them to me and told me to try each of them on.

"Boaz, you have done an excellent job. These boots feel better than any I have ever had," I told him. "How do you take an old camel's hide, which has both tough and tender areas, and come out with such leather that seems to breathe for your feet when you walk?"

"I'm glad you said that your feet breathe when you walk, because that is exactly what they must do to be comfortable," he informed me. All of my leather is prepared by my people at the 'Good Samaritan Oasis.' They are the secret to my shoes feeling so pleasant to wear."

"Boaz, the last time I was here, you told me that sometime you would tell me why you built this new store and cobbler shop," I began.

"Well, it is a long story, but I have wanted to tell you ever since we became such close friends," he said. "My leather is the best in the world because my people cure and tan it better than anyone. They have been doing it for a hundred years," he said.

"Why don't you tell me about your people, Boaz?"

"I am of Hebrew ancestry. My people have always been a wandering people. When my father was a very young man, he lived on an oasis in the desert. He married my Mother and they decided to leave the desert country and go to the city to start a 'shoe cobbler shop.' They packed up their few belongings on one camel and went North, across the desert to Egypt. After they had been there for a few years, they heard of some good people who had a strong religious faith, who lived even further North. For several months, they traveled through many countries and finally reached their destination, nearly 3,000 miles. They settled near the Southern border of Lithuania, at the capital city, Vilnius.

"My father, Boaz, Sr., started a cobbler shop in that city and imported leather that was made by his folks back at the 'Good Samaritan Oasis.' The shoes in his shop were the best in all the country of Lithuania. Within a few months, people from all the countries around the Baltic Sea began coming to my father's shop for shoes and boots. He opened a camel store which sold camel boots, camel coats, camel rugs and camel ivory jewelry.

"His camel store was the largest shoe and camel store in all the country. My parents became very wealthy from operating their store. Even the King of Lithuania heard about the camel store and he went there to have boots and a camel coat made for himself, and jewelry made for the Queen.

"Before long, the good Christian king became very good friends with the good Christian cobbler, who he called 'the little shoe cobbler.' One day as the little cobbler was walking near the king's castle, the king saw him and invited the little shoe cobbler to the back veranda of his castle. They sat and talked about the state of the kingdom. The little cobbler spoke bravely and honestly as friend to friend. The king

120

insisted that the little cobbler come to see him each day and that he and the queen would be waiting for him.

"Every afternoon, the little cobbler went to the king's veranda and told him the news of the common man on the street. The good king welcomed the news, since it helped him to govern his kingdom properly.

"Beautiful gates with posted, uniformed guards stood at the front entrance to the castle, but there were no gates or guards at the back, private entrance. One day, the captain of the guards insisted that a beautiful gate be built at the rear of the castle and that guards be placed there also. Without thinking, the good king agreed.

"When the little cobbler came to the gate with guarded soldiers, he turned around and went back home. For three days, the king and queen waited for the little cobbler to come for his daily visit. But, the little cobbler always went back home as soon as he was approached by the guards.

"On the fourth day, the little cobbler went dressed properly to enter the beautiful gate. He had on his high-top boots and flipped out collar shirt, and his most expensive camel's wool coat. He was properly attired for a formal visit to his king and queen. He passed the guards and made his way to the veranda where he greeted the king and queen in a royal fashion.

"But the little cobbler would not sit and talk freely with the king. He did not feel comfortable under those circumstances. The king missed the little cobbler's advice and candid conversation, but the little cobbler did not feel that it was right to criticize the building of the formal gate to the back of the veranda. He never mentioned the obstruction at any time.

"During the night, the king suddenly realized the problem between him and the little cobbler. Early the next morning, he summoned the captain of the guards and told him to take down the gate that led to the back veranda. The captain objected because of their beauty and dignity. But the king prevailed and the gate came down.

"The next evening, the king and queen sat on the back veranda, looking in the direction of the little cobbler's shop. They waited and looked until nearly dark. Then suddenly, he said, 'Oh Queen, Oh Queen, I see a beautiful sight.' The queen asked him if they were rebuilding the beautiful gate

121

again. The King said, 'It is more beautiful than that.' The queen asked again what he saw that was so beautiful. 'It is the little cobbler, dressed in his little cobbler suit who is coming to help me govern my kingdom.'"

Boaz was silent for a while. I sat almost breathless. Then he spoke again. "That little cobbler was my Father. My Mother told me this story many years ago and I shall pass it on to my children and grandchildren."

"That's a wonderful and beautiful story, Boaz," I said. "I'm glad you told me about your people."

"For many years my father continued to run his camel shop and visited the king every day, helping him to keep in touch with the man on the street. Then, the Communists from the North invaded the little country, drove the good king from his throne and made Lithuania a Communist satellite country. My father had to give his business and everything he had worked for to the Communist government. At the first opportunity, my parents left Lithuania and came back to the 'Good Samaritan Oasis,' where they lived out the rest of their lives with their kindred."

Boaz thought for a while before he finished his story. "I was a young man in those days and when we resettled in the desert, I married Rebekah and brought her to this Fringe country. We are still very close to our kindred and visit them often. I told you this story of my family so you may see why I am a cobbler and why I wanted a good camel store like my father before me.

"Boaz," I said. "I like your new store and especially since I have heard about the foundation it is built upon. Surely, this is the 'Greatest Camel Store on Earth.' It is a benefit to all the people in the Fringe country and a part of each of our lives."

I paid Boaz for my new boots but told him not to wrap them. "I want to wear them home," I said. "I must show these beautiful boots to Anna. They are surely the most comfortable boots in the world."

I Am A Camel Specialist!

For a number of years I had harbored a secret dream of speaking to the American Veterinary Medical Association. As a visitor one time, I was able to say a few impromptu words to the delegates, but I longed to be able to present a dissertation on my old friend, the camel. Sure enough, I finally received an official invitation from the AVMA to speak at their annual convention one summer.

Anna and I arranged our furlough to coincide with the convention. I had studied and prepared for the speech and looked forward to the meeting. When the time came, however, I came down with a case of old-fashioned stage fright and wondered how I would be able to perform before those six thousand delegates.

When the chairman rapped his gavel on the podium to call the convention to order, I knew that according to the program, I would have a little time before my speech. Each speaker spoke briefly about his specialty; the cow specialist, the dog specialist, the horse specialist and others. Then he told the delegates that for the first time in the history of the AVMA, they would hear about an animal that had never been on the program before.

Finally, I heard the chairman announce, "Now we will hear from Dr. William J. Isabell, a camel specialist, from Ethiopia, Africa." There was the usual round of applause as I made my way to the podium. I gave a cordial thanks for being invited to speak, but I admitted that when I looked out on their sea of faces, I had become speechless.

"How many of you have ever doctored a camel? I asked. "Please raise your hand!" Not a single hand was raised but mine.

"Let me ask you another question. How many of you plan to include the camel in your future practice?" Again, I asked them to respond by raising their hands. Yet, not one single hand was raised, except my own.

"Since none of you are now treating camels and none of you ever expect to include the camel in your practice," I said jokingly, "I'll just discard the scientific information and tips about the camel. No one here needs these findings so they are useless. I already know what they say, so I'll just put them here in my pocket and when I am through, I'll deposit them in the closest waste can." Everyone laughed when I shoved my notes into my pocket.

"Since I do not have a prepared speech now, I'll just tell you randomly about the camel, one of the finest animals that the Lord ever created in His world.

123

"From the very beginning, the camel has been known as a 'beast of burden' and in more than four thousand years, he has not changed in his work patterns or his usefulness to man. He is probably the only animal in the world who has not undergone scientific or laboratory testing in order to improve him genetically. As far as I know, there has never been any controlled breeding to shorten his legs, or to improve his rough stride, or to give him a newer cosmetic face to improve his chances in a beauty contest.

"None of these scientific endeavors would help to improve the camel or his usefulness to man. So, we must conclude, 'No changes needed here.'

"The camel was specifically created for the desert. He can store a large supply of water, endure the heat and sand of the desert, and protect himself, his cargo and his rider from the many desert storms that may threaten him. The camel has been known to survive in the hot desert storms for as long as twenty days, yet bring himself, his rider and his cargo to safety. How can we scientifically improve his make-up for desert living? We can't. So we must again conclude, 'No changes needed here.'

"My friend, the camel, has eyelids and eyelashes which protect him from the desert sun and wind while traveling. He has kneepads on his legs that protect them from the rough sand while kneeling. He can drink salty water, eat thorny bushes in the desert, and has no digestive disturbances or diseases which require immunizations. What changes are needed to improve his health? I asked. "None. 'No changes needed.'

"You can readily see that the camel does not need a veterinarian. Yet, in my practice in the Fringe country of Ethiopia, I have appointed myself as a kind of camel specialist, but I admit, that even today after more than twenty years, I am a bit afraid of the camel.

"When I see a camel coming up the road from the direction of the desert, I have mixed emotions. I am elated with joy that he is coming to my clinic for some minor repair. But, on the other hand, I secretly wish that he would pass me by because of my constant, inward fear of the huge animal.

"Usually, the camel does not need a veterinarian, but he does need the veterinarian to understand that as long as

124

there are deserts to cross, and as long as there are men who must cross those deserts, there will be a need for camels.

"Let me conclude," I told the audience, "by reminding each of you that among these three: the man, the desert, and the camel, the greatest miracle is probably the camel. Miracles do not change, but miracles do cause changes in the hearts of men. I know that the miracle of the camel has caused a change in my own heart."

I thanked the audience and sat down. All the delegates stood in a standing ovation, not for me, but for the camel.

"Doctor," the program chairman asked. "Did you bring a delegation from Africa with you to this meeting?"

"No sir," I replied. "Just my wife Anna."

Anna was asked to come to the podium and she stood by my side as the chairman introduced her. "You wife, Anna, is delegation enough," he said. "She is beautiful!"

I was happy that day because my camel, my wife, and I had been "International" guests of the American Veterinary Medical Association.

Rode the Camel Eight Days

It was in the fall one year as the summer plants and pasture growth began dying. Most of the Fringe country farmers had been taught to give special attention to their cattle, sheep and goats during this time of the year. There are several diseases and discomforts which usually attack just before the winter months begin.

Even the old camel, despite his rarity of sickness, needs to be closely observed during this time of the year. He has the ability to withstand diverse temperature changes better than all other animals. His degree of allowance is eleven degrees above or below any other animal. Even the cold weather does not have any adverse effect on him and his digestive problems are almost unknown.

When the front door of the clinic opened one morning, I greeted Dr. Ling who was returning from a call in the country.

"Have you seen Boaz yet this morning?" he asked me.

"No, I haven't. Does he need me?"

"Well, you know Boaz. He never bothers anyone unless he has a good reason," Ling replied. "But, something is disturbing him. I can tell by the way he is so quiet."

I got my wide-brimmed Western straw hat and headed for Boaz' house in the Jeep. When I got to his store, he was looking out the window and rushed out to greet me.

"Hi, Boaz," I greeted him. "Why are you stepping so lively this morning?"

"I need you, Mr. Cow Doctor, to do something for me," he replied.

"Just name it and I will get it done!"

"One of my relatives from the desert was here yesterday afternoon and told me that many of the cows at the "Good Samaritan Oasis' are sick and some have already died," he told me. "They want you and me to come and see if we can stop them from dying."

"That's fine. When shall we leave?" I asked.

"We'll have to ride the camels across the desert," he told me. "We should leave at day-break tomorrow."

The next morning at daybreak, Boaz was waiting in the driveway of the clinic. He had three big camels, standing in line, waiting to be loaded. They had been fed and watered, each of them drinking thirty gallons of water in preparation for the desert trip.

I had carefully packed my instruments and drugs with anticipation of any disease that I had ever treated in more than twenty years in the Fringe country.

"Boaz, will you have your load camel to kneel down in a loading position for me to put my supplies in place," I asked.

The big camel slowly bent his front feet and then lowered his hind legs to a sitting position on Boaz' command. "I'll do the loading," he said, "so the load will be evenly distributed."

I climbed on the second camel as directed by my friend and then Boaz mounted the first camel in the caravan. The load camel in the rear was tied to mine.

The first day of riding the camel took its toll on me. It seemed to be a rough and constant swaying ride. I thought the old camel had been out on the desert so long, he must have lost his ability to "sail as the ship of the desert," as the camel is known. Then I realized that many ships were for cargo and not for the comfort of man's ride.

I watched and counted as I noticed the old camel move both right feet forward and then both left feet forward, repeating the process over and over, swaying from one side to the other. It was very unlike the horse who moves one left and one right foot in unison, giving the rider a smoother ride.

Each night we stopped our small caravan about sundown, so that during the twilight we would have time to eat our supper and bed down for the night. There was really nothing to do except eat our flat cake of millet bread with curry chicken, followed with small millet cakes and sweet cane sugar. The only thing we had to drink with our meals was water, which we carried in three large stone containers, one strapped to each camel, in the event one would be broken.

I used the time just before bedtime to watch the camels prepare for the night. We loosened the girth-latches a little for the comfort of the camels. They each turned around in two or three directions several times as though they were checking on the best lying position.

"The camels are checking the wind current," Boaz told me. "They always lay with their heads toward the wind."

I noticed that all the camels were lying in the same direction but it was not very comfortable. I finally got behind the big camel and fell asleep for a full night's rest.

The next morning, we arose before daybreak and ate our food just as the sun was rising. We wanted to get in a full day of caravaning. Each day, we repeated the pattern of the first and on the fourth day, we finally arrived at the "Good Samaritan Oasis" about noontime.

We were greeted warmly by the people of the oasis who gave us tasty, fig-like bread as a snack. I slipped two of those little "tidbits" into my secret pocket for Anna to sample when I got home. We went straight to the area where the cattle were gathered, under a tree which was ten degrees cooler than out in the hot desert sun.

"Where are the sick cows?" I asked.

"It's not really the cows," one of the leaders volunteered. "It's all our young cattle that are just sick and some are dying every few days. We have lost almost half of our young calves from this trouble."

I saw one calf prostrate on the ground. On closer examination, it looked like "blackleg disease," which was very common in many areas of the world. To be sure, I had to do a postmortem of the muscles of the limb. Sure enough, there was a dark, mushy,raised area of the limb muscle.

We caught every calf in the oasis and vaccinated them with blackleg vaccine. The older cows were not susceptible to blackleg because of the mature makeup of the muscle tissue. I was sure that none of the healthy calves would suffer from the disease now that they had been inoculated.

The next morning, Boaz' kin folks came to our tent with breakfast and offered to show us around the oasis. It was like a "garden of Eden," with luscious grapes and figs hanging on the vines. There were sorghum, millet, and barley from the fields. Many beautiful vegetables were growing in the garden, located near the stream of water that fed the oasis.

I saw water pumps and ramps which were brought from Cairo, Egypt, and now were being used to irrigate the fertile areas everyday. Even though the water pumps were hand driven, the work was shared on a rotating basis by several attendants.

We thanked our hosts cordially and the camels were loaded with beautiful tanned leather used by Boaz in his camel shop. The trip home was another four day ride. The ride seemed smoother, however, probably because I sat on several layers of soft, new camel leather.

The best part of the trip was seeing Anna standing in the doorway waiting for me to return. I jumped down from the camel, rushed to her, and held her tightly until my arms hurt.

Six months later, I heard that there had been no more deaths among the calves and the herd was doing fine. Also, the "Good Samaritan Oasis" community issued a proclamation to me. Boaz and Rebekah brought it to me and after calling Anna, Ling and Sal, he bowed graciously to me and began to read:

Proclamation

Dr. Bill (Mr. Cow Doctor)

We of the Good Samaritan Oasis kindred owe a debt of gratitude to Dr. Bill for saving our cattle herds, and came to us when we were in need.

If you are ever in need, Dr. Bill, just "Ask and you shall receive."

From all of us in the Oasis, and from our one hundred camels, we lift their heads proudly in your direction.

Chapter Twelve

Practice Like a Vet

Cows Bloated — Ego Deflated

ONE SUMMER while home on furlough, Dr. Mac had an urgent call at nine o'clock in the morning from a Mr. John Porter. He had a cow whose stomach had become bloated and we knew that one of the most urgent calls for a vet is one involving a bloated cow.

We were at Mr. Porter's farm within twenty minutes after he called. He took us to the cow, which was near the barn, and our first inclination was to pass a large tube into the cow's stomach and hope the gas formation would expel. When the tube was inserted, we hit the kind of bloat that immediately discharged the gas as fast as letting the air from a basket ball. To finish our treatment, we gave the cow an antiferment agent.

From the top of a hill, one of the young men who worked for Mr. Porter called to tell us that another cow was also bloated. We quickly moved to the second cow, and passed the tube into its stomach to relieve the gas formation. Then we applied the antiferment before going on to the next cow. This process was repeated seven times before we were through.

Before we had finished with all the cows, several local people had gathered around us to observe the treatment. They were astonished as they heard and smelled the sharp odor of the gas as it was discharged.

131

"This gas is very similar to the natural gas which we burn in our homes," Dr. Mac told one of the young boys who was standing nearby. Mac took a match and quickly ignited the expelling gas at the end of the stomach tube which was inserted into the cow. A large blue flame appeared from the tube. After a while the gas diminished and the flame went out. One young boy grabbed the end of the tube and hollered, "Put that fire out! It will run back inside the cow and kill her!"

Dr. Mac tried to explain that there was no danger because it was impossible to burn anything without oxygen, which was not present in the cow's stomach.

Later, when I had returned to the Fringe country, a similar call came to me. It was nine o'clock one morning when Hugo came running to me to come help his cow. It was the only cow Hugo had. We jumped into the Jeep, drove to his farm, and after inserting the stomach tube, the gas was discharged and the antiferment agent was applied.

The next day, the same cow became bloated and I treated her again. This happened for six days straight and I used many different drugs to prevent this reoccurrence. On the last day, I tried a new drug which contained enzymes, which were to aid digestion and help control fermentation. When I went back to check on the cow the next day to see the results from the new drug, the cow was normal and there was no bloat.

I felt very elated and proud of my accomplishment with the new drug. As I was leaving, Hugo said, "She's all right today, Doctor Bill. I knew she would be okay because last night, I gave her an old, dirty dish rag to chew on."

My ego was deflated more than the bloated cow's stomach!

The Cow Has Low Sugar

On another occasion while working at Dr. Mac's clinic, we made a call to treat a cow that had acetonemia, or low sugar. Of course, there is always hope that in breeding a milk cow for high production, that the balance of sugar or calcium in her body would not be upset.

It is always important to try to pay special attention to those cows in a dairy herd which show the grave symptoms of acetonemia. This condition results from a cow producing more milk volume than her body can take in as feed, then to metabolize it without problems.

The cow we were to treat was a very high producer. When we approached her we noticed that she had a jumping, nervous motion and her breath had a sweet acetone odor. She continued licking her lips with her tongue, making circular motions in the air. We knew that licking with her tongue was almost a pathognamonic symptom the cow had acetonemia.

We treated the cow with glucose in the vein. Then Dr. Mac told the owner to put one quart of black strap molasses on her feed everyday for the next few days. Three days later, when we went back to that farm to check on some of the other cows in the herd, we saw a cow that seemed to have balls of straw around all four feet.

"What's wrong with that cow over there?" he said as he pointed to the strange looking sight. "It looks like she has four, hay-balled feet."

"Oh, she's doing fine," the owner explained. "That's the same cow you told me to put one quart of black strap molasses on her feet daily!"

The man had apparently "misheard" or Dr. Mac had "misspoken" when he gave the instructions. At any rate, the cow was getting plenty of exercise in her hay-balled feet!

Again in the Fringe country, I had an occasion to treat one cow for acetonemia, which showed the same symptoms as the one I had encountered at Dr. Mac's in Tennessee.

The owner of this cow, however, could not speak English very well. "My cow sickie, lickie, and no eatie," he told me waving his hands. "Lickie and no eatie," he exclaimed.

I knew the probable diagnosis: I had a cow with low sugar to treat that day.

Arsenic Trioxide — There is no Antidote!

In the summer of 1961 while practicing for Dr. Mac, I received a call that a herd of Holstein dairy cows were sick in the next county. When I arrived at the designated farm, I saw thirty or forty cows down on the ground. Some were in the process of dying while others had already died.

I jumped out of the car and went immediately to the first dying cow. When I smelled the breath of the first cow, I vividly remembered such an odor more than twenty years before. It smelled exactly like arsenic trioxide.

It was when I was about eighteen years old and working with several other boys in Mr. Cook's new rat-killing business. He pulled a trailer behind his car that had a picture of a rat, lying on its back to show it was dead. We boys worked in his basement, filling up bottles of arsenic trioxide and were told to always use rubber gloves and avoid letting the chemical touch our body in any way.

Mr. Cook was a super-salesman. He would pull his trailer into a town and then visit the hardware and drug stores, asking them to let him leave at least four bottles of his "rat killer" in their store. Out on the street, he would stop some innocent person and offer them a dollar if they would go into the store and ask for his rat poison. After getting two or three responses within the first few hours, the store owners wanted to stock several more bottles of his rat killer.

The chemical was to be put into a small dish and when the rat ran across the dish, it would slightly burn his feet. When the rat licked his irritated feet, he would be licking the arsenic trioxide, which would kill him immediately.

The chemical was also used to kill weeds and bushes along fence rows and was even used to kill the weeds along the railroads. It was a very dangerous poison and was totally outlawed in most of the U.S. in the middle 1940s.

I was sure that the smell I remembered when a high school student matched this same odor on this cow. I told the owner that I believed his cattle had arsenic trioxide poisoning, and that there was no effective antidote!

I immediately called the state and federal veterinarian offices and they were on the scene within an hour. I told them about my diagnosis but neither of them was familiar with that kind of poisoning. Several other county veterinarians also arrived. Lab tests confirmed the presence of arsenic trioxide.

We were all puzzled and wondered how this poison got here. I examined the roadsides and found that the county had sprayed for weeds along the road and up to the fence posts the day before this tragedy. We went to the county garage and sure enough, we found the cans of weed killer, "Arsenic

Trioxide" with the familiar skull and crossbones beneath the name.

Mr. Hood and his son lost ninety one of his fine Holstein cows through this mishap. He only had eleven left. But, the county had insurance which paid for the loss.

In the county road office, we found an advertisement in a magazine for an effective weed killer. It read: "Bush Killer for sale. Guaranteed to kill all types of weeds and bushes. Warning: will kill deer on Railroad right of way and cannot be used by Railroad. Will sell for the price of shipping."

The county had bought the bush kill in good faith that it would kill the weeds and bushes along their road ways. It did kill those unwanted weeds, but it also killed a herd of fine cattle.

After doing all I could about the sick cows, I sat down on a milk stool in the barn alongside Mr. Hood. The barn, which had been filled with cattle only the day before, was now empty. I wept, along with Mr. Hood. I had known the dangerous effect of that chemical more than twenty years before and I wondered, *Why hadn't I tried to do something about it then?*

A 2 P.M. Appointment

On another occasion while caring for Dr. Mac's practice, I was called by a Mr. Jackson to treat a cow for "foot rot." He told me not to come until after 2:00 p.m.

"I watch a television program everyday from 1:30 to 2," Mr. Jackson told me. "Today, I'm sure that this mean fellow, Brad Murdock, is going to be found guilty of murder. I don't want to miss this episode.'

"I'll be there after two o'clock," I promised him.

I got to his farm, treated his cow, and was ready to leave when I asked, "Well, did Brad Murdock draw a heavy sentence for the murder rap on your TV program?"

"No! Would you believe that the lawyer for the defense claimed to have new evidence to prove him innocent, even though ten people saw him commit the murder?" he answered disgustingly.

By a strange coincidence, two years later when on furlough, I was again called to Mr. Jackson's farm to treat a sick cow — after 2 p.m., of course. I was told again that the murder trial for Brad Murdock should end today and that Mr. Jackson wanted to see the program.

While treating the sick cow, I asked Mr. Jackson, "Did that mean Brad Murdock finally get his sentence?"

"Brad Murdock has a real slick lawyer that got him off again today. This has been three years of trial and everytime we just about get to the verdict of guilty, the lawyer comes up with a new wrinkle," the farmer said. "I'm going to stay with this trial until we hang that crooked Murdock, if it takes another twenty years!"

On the way back to the clinic I thought about the soap opera and the millions of people like Mr. Jackson who watched the program everyday. If the people who watched the program everyday would buy two bars of soap every year for twenty years, the advertiser would still be very rich, even though they had to continue paying a "slick lawyer" to continually stall the case.

Friend of Potentate

I had been a member of the African Animal Association for twenty years. This large body of African citizens from all over the continent are charged with the preservation, protection and recognition of animals in Africa. Beside myself, the only other bona-fide member I knew personally was Boaz. who had been a member for more than thirty years. Each year we went to the meetings specifically to propagate one animal, the camel.

The annual meeting of this national organization was usually held in a large, more populated city in Central or South Africa. The convention was never held in the Northern one-third of the continent, because most of the area is desert. To the North of the Fringe country is the Sahara Desert and just across the Red sea is the vast deserts of Saudi Arabia.

For Boaz and I, the most exciting time of the entire convention was the nomination for the animal of the year. This was always a popularity contest. Even though the camel is important in the African continent, he never had a large delegation of support in attendance at the conventions. Of course, the camel lives in or near the desert where the support population at the convention was few in number.

Few of the desert people who own camels attended the conventions, even though the camel population in Ethiopia alone is reported to be some 800,000. Boaz and I tried to represent the camels at the conventions and tried for years to bring home a "Blue Ribbon" to our beloved camel! But, we had never been successful.

The delegates at the convention knew me as the man with the perennial camel nomination every year. When the chairman of the convention would open up the floor for nominations for the animal of the year, I was usually first on my feet.

"Mr. Chairman, I nominate the camel!" I would say.

Every year, I nominated the same animal. When the delegates would see me rise for the nomination, they would almost repeat in unison, "I nominate the camel!" But then after several more popular animals were nominated, the vote would be taken. The camel never won or even came close to winning. Every year the camel lost, but I was not too hurt over the vote. Let's face it. The camel is not the most handsome animal in the world, neither is he very swift of foot.

"Someday our camel is going to win that Blue Ribbon, Dr. Bill," Boaz would comfort me. He had never failed to vote with me for the camel. He and his family had strong religious ties to the camel. To him and his kindred, there was a recognized link of sacredness which the Lord must have given to their whole clan and their camels.

Then one year, Boaz went to the convention one week earlier than I. I wondered why it was necessary to be at the convention grounds so early but I didn't push the question. The convention, for the first time that year, was held in the Kruger National Park in the Northeastern part of South Africa. The convention center was a beautiful, large rectangular building with a large, open display for various animals.

When I arrived, none of the animals were in the roped off display area. I saw Boaz at a table with some of the program officials preparing the final details of the convention.

"Hi Boaz," I said with pleasure, noting that he seemed to be making friends with the convention's big "potentate."

"I have been working on some of the convention details and I have something for you to do, Dr. Bill," he told me.

"I'll do whatever you say," I assured him.

"When they ask for nominations for the animal of the year, I want you to nominate the camel," he instructed.

"I'll sure do that all right," I replied. "But I do nominate our beloved camel every year. What is so different about today?"

"You'll see," he said with a twinkle in his eyes.

From the podium, we all heard the chairman rap his gavel. "Could I have your attention please? This session will now come to order," he commanded. "Our first item of business is to hear a report from the animal of the year rules committee." The chairman looked in Boaz' direction. Boaz then rose to speak.

"As head of the rules committee, we want to be fair to all the animals and we believe that this year we should honor those animals which not only help man, but are best suited to their work and habitat," Boaz explained. "For example, the camel is the only animal that is suited to the desert sand, heat and travel, and can survive during water and food shortages."

After a few questions and answers, Boaz sat down and the chairman opened the floor for nominations of the animals of the year, using the new ground rules. As soon as he was through talking, I jumped to my feet.

"Mr. Chairman, I nominate the camel, that great beast of burden of the desert for more than 4,000 years."

The delegates at the assembly, who already had their notes and pads ready to nominate another animal, were suddenly still. One by one they began to stand to second the nomination of the camel. Then, after a few moments, a respected member of the association for many years rose to his feet.

"Mr. Chairman," he began slowly. "With all fairness in my heart and a deep love for all animals, I move that the nominations cease and that we elect the camel as our animal of the year by acclamation!"

The members of the convention all voiced their vote with a resounding "Aye!" After the non-contested vote, Boaz went to the microphone again.

138

"As chairman of the selection committee," he announced, "I would like for all of us to move to the animal display grounds so I can award the winning Blue Ribbon to the deserving camel."

At the display grounds, there were a large number of camels already assembled, each with their drivers, lined in neat rows.

"What is the 'camel power' of this unit?" Boaz asked the head driver.

"It is 100 camel power," he answered.

"And what is the useful life expectancy of each 'filament?'"

"Fifty years," the lead driver responded.

Then Boaz clipped a blue ribbon on the "fare-lock" of each of the camels and handed each camel rider two pieces of silver. The slow moving caravan of 100 camels fell into single file as they left in the direction of their home — the Fringe country and the Good Samaritan Oasis. All the drivers were kindred of Boaz and proudly listed their lineage from Abraham, Isaac, and Jacob. That day, they had upheld the honor of their beloved camel even as their forefathers had done many years before.

Chapter Thirteen

All Kept Their Appointments

Old Sally Won the Blue Ribbon

One day at Dr. Mac's, ten-year-old Tommy Woodard talked with Dr. Mac on the phone. He wanted us to come see their milk cow named "Old Sally."

"You remember where we live, don't you, Dr. Mac?" he asked. "I'm Jim Woodard's son."

"Yes," Mac replied. "I remember you, your father and even Old Sally, your Jersey cow. I'll be there about 2 p.m," I heard him tell Tommy.

When we arrived at the Woodard farm, we saw Mr. Woodard, Tommy and five members of his ball team, and Old Sally, the Jersey milk cow standing by the fence which separated the little ball field from the small cow pasture.

"My son and his ball team wanted to call you," Mr. Woodard told us. "They said Old Sally is breathing very heavy, as though her left nostril is stopped up! And she has a nasal drainage that seems abnormal."

"Yes, something is wrong," Dr. Mac told them. We then held Old Sally's head in an upward position and used a scope light to see into the nostril that showed impairment. A long, gray object was blocking the nasal passage. We then used forceps to grasp the object and a piece of wood was extracted from the nasal passage and Old Sally breathed normal again. Tommy and his teammates were watching the operation about ten feet from us. One of the little boys cried, "They found the stick!" You could see their happiness by the expressions on their faces.

The whole delegation of youngsters approached Mr. Woodard for a time of explanation. Tommy began talking. "We were playing with Old Sally as we do everyday when we get tired of playing baseball," he explained. "We were using that stick to tickle her nose and someway, she breathed too heavy and the stick disappeared up her nose. We tried, but couldn't get it out."

Tommy stood between his dad and Old Sally and touched both of them as he talked. He wanted both of them to realize that they did not mean any harm from their poor judgment in playing.

As we began to leave, Tommy and his team approached us. "Here is some money for coming to see Old Sally," they offered. Dr. Mac would not accept their money for the call. Mr. Woodard told the boys to take the old stick and put it on the woodpile. While the boys were gone, he told Dr. Mac to accept the money when they came back. He believed that they needed to learn that they were responsible for their mistakes.

When the boys returned, they gave the money to Dr. Mac and he put it into his pocket. As we were about to pull out of the driveway, the boys ran after the truck, waving for us to stop.

"We're afraid that you did not let us pay you enough for this call," they said. Each boy had his hand extended toward Dr. Mac, each holding a few coins.

"No, you paid enough," Dr. Mac assured them. "But, I have a new curry-comb and hair brush I would like to give you to keep Old Sally groomed. She is such a good cow and very beautiful."

On my next furlough, Mr. Woodard came into the clinic and invited Dr. Mac and I to go with him to the county fair grounds. When we arrived, the dairy cattle show was in progress. We saw the little baseball team with Old Sally and she looked more beautiful than ever. She was well fed and groomed, with a new brown leather halter decorated with brass studs. Her lead rein was a beautiful woven flax and rice straw. No doubt about it, the boys had fed, groomed and trained her for the entire year. Besides being a beautiful cow, she also had good qualities as a Jersey milk cow.

The judges finally finished their individual inspection tour and the winners were about to be announced. The final prize, the Blue Ribbon for first place, was announced over the public address system.

"The Blue Ribbon goes to a Jersey milk cow, Old Sally, sponsored by Old Sally's baseball team." There was a solid round of applause and Tommy and his teammates waved to Mr. Woodard and us in triumph. They felt they had done what was right to amend for the one poor judgement when playing with Old Sally's nostril.

There was Old Sally, standing proudly looking at her baseball team. She seemed to know that she was well fed, well groomed, and could compete with any other cow in the show. It was a perfect picture with the team members crowded around Old Sally with her Blue Ribbon flowing from her halter buckle.

Jenny Lind Moved Our Cows

On one occasion, I was helping Dr. Mac give vaccinations to several cows and their calves before turning them out into the spring pasture. The farm where we were treating the heard was located on the Old Stage Coach Turnpike in Robertson County, Tennessee. This was the road which used to connect New Orleans and Louisville. Near the road, the Old Stage Coach building was still standing.

We had almost completed our work when we noticed a caravan of buses, automobiles and limousines approaching us. As they got out of their vehicles, the group of dignitaries seemed surprised that we were using the front yard and the old Inn as a cow barn and cattle pen. One of the leaders asked if we would be through with our work shortly.

When we finished vaccinating the last calves, we drove them out to the pasture behind the old Inn. Then we decided to stay around and see what they were going to do. The group gathered in a large semi-circle and waited for the leader to begin his speech.

"We thank all of you for coming to the dedication of this old stone platform," he began. "This is the only registered place in the United States that Jenny Lind sang as a brilliant concert opera star. One hundred years ago today, Miss Lind sang for the guests at this Stage Coach Inn. According to the National Historical Records, which was registered by the

143

owner of this Inn, she gave a twenty minute concert from this platform on June 6, 1851.

"This is where the American monument to Miss Jenny Lind will stand," he declared while the dignitaries applauded.

Three years later, a new and greater monument was completed with a beautiful exhibit building. It has become a place of pride for all people of America. The stone platform, which we used to vaccinate the cattle has been retained as a remembrance of where she stood.

As an after note for any who may not be familiar with Jenny Lind, (1820-1887), she was a Swedish Soprano, who became the most famous singer of the 1800s. She had a brilliant career in opera and concerts with her warm contralto voice and unique vocal control.

Miss Lind won the title, "The Swedish Nightingale," and toured the U.S. from 1850 to 1852, under the management of the renowned P. T. Barnum.

Sunday Morning Cow Bath

One Sunday morning, Ray West, a dear friend of Dr. Mac had milked his dairy herd as usual. Before leaving the barn to get ready for church, Ray grabbed his spray can and gave each cow a good spraying to keep the flies controlled for the day.

As Mr. West was preparing to leave for church, he looked toward the cow lot. He noticed that all twenty cows had either fallen down on the ground or were staggering around the lot as if they were drunk.

He turned the car around, went back to the house and called Dr. Mac to his home. Ray described the symptoms to Dr. Mac and asked him to get to his farm as fast as possible.

When Dr. Mac arrived at the West farm, he noticed a peculiar odor from the cows. "What is that odor?" he asked.

"Oh, I know what it is," Ray remembered. "I've used the crop poison spray instead of the fly spray!"

The best antidote would be to give the twenty cows a thorough bath with soap and water. The pores of the skin had to be opened quickly or the cows would all die. It would be impossible for Dr. Mac and Ray to bathe all the cows within an hour. Many of the cows would probably die from the poisoning.

Ray lived about one-half mile from the church and decided to jump in his car and try to get a couple of men to help him in his predicament. The service was in progress but Ray went quietly to two of his friends and whispered his request. Just then, the preacher noticed the commotion and stopped the service.

"Brother West, would you care to tell the congregation why there is so much commotion," the kindly preacher asked.

Ray quickly told the group about his plight. Then the preacher said, "There are about 100 men here today. I think we'll dismiss our service, go home and get into our work clothes, and meet at Brother Ray's house in twenty minutes."

Some started arriving within a few minutes, while others, who lived further away came as soon as possible. They came with brushes, buckets and soap powder and quickly began to wash the cows until they were completely clean. Within a few minutes the cows began to stand up, which assured the large, happy group that the effects of the poison was gone.

The preacher asked for everyone's attention. "We have the 'ox out of the ditch,'" he said. "This will conclude the service which was begun at the church and moved to the cow pasture. My text for this morning's sermon, which I did not get to preach, was 'Am I My Brother's Keeper?' Seeing the wonderful response from the congregation, it is unnecessary to preach that sermon.

"Now, let us bow our heads for the benediction. 'Dear Lord, thank You for such a quick answer to the sermon I was going to preach!'"

The Camel Is the Meanest of All!

I really don't want to mention some of the things I must say about my beloved camel, but I must be honest. While the camel is the great burden bearer and the most useful of animals, I must admit that he is one of the ugliest and meanest of all animals.

The old, romantic thoughts of the camel are well deserved, but his personal appearance is not all that romantic. He has a shaggy coat, is humpbacked, awkward, stiff-legged, popeyed and to say the least, he is just plain ugly.

Like some other animals, he chews the cud. But, unlike other animals, the camel has teeth at the center front of the upper jaw and can bite with severe damage. Without horns or antlers, this ability to bite gives the camel a compensatory advantage. Also, if this cud-chewing camel is ill treated by anyone, he will spit a foul-smelling cud into the person's face. Let me tell you a story about a spitting camel.

My friend Boaz has a cousin with two camels, who lives about twenty miles from our clinic in the Fringe country. He asked me to make a veterinarian call on his camel. Because I did not know the way to his house, I asked Boaz to go with me on the call. I had been told that the camel was not sick internally, but had a sore-like injury on its back, near the center of its hump.

When we arrived at Boaz' cousins house, everyone had gone to help a neighbor in the millet harvest.

"It is good that I came with you, Brother Bill" Boaz told me. "You will need me to help you treat the camel. Since my cousin James has two camels, we shall put the cargo harness and small platform on the other camel's back. Then, we can put the two camels close together."

It sure was a good thing that he had come with me. I wouldn't have known how to handle the camels by myself and certainly would not have thought about using one camel to service the other.

"Now, Dr. Bill, you can get on this deck and you will be able to reach the other camel with no difficulty,"Boaz told me as he commanded the extra camel to kneel.

When I was in place on the cargo deck of the second camel, I could see the infected area of the ailing camel. It looked like the problem was caused by the rubbing of a girth strap that had not been properly tightened. I cleaned the area of the sore while both of the camels stood rigidly still.

Next, I applied an antibiotic and began to think that the sore looked very similar to fungus infection. I knew that I must try to put some iodine on the sore spot. But, I also knew that when I did, I would have to hold on tightly to my camel, just in case the injured one began to act up.

As soon as the iodine was applied on the camel's back, it began whinnying and crying. Then, thinking the other camel had hurt him, he began spitting the foul-smelling cud into the camel's face. Also, he began biting him and a real fight ensued. Boaz, seeing I was in trouble, picked up a big stick and threatened the emotional camels to stop, while at the same time rescuing me from atop the cargo deck.

But, that wasn't the end of it. As soon as I was free, they began fighting again, biting, kicking, spitting, all initiated by the injured camel. The fight would subside for a while, but before long, the injured camel started again on the poor, innocent other camel. Boaz separated them several times.

With our job done, we got back into the Jeep and started the motor for our return trip. "Stop the Jeep," Boaz commanded. "I'm going to ride my cousins other camel home and keep him for a few days. If I don't, this mad camel will keep this fight going for a week."

I left in the Jeep alone and Boaz would start the long, ten-hour trip home atop the other camel. It was just another proof that Boaz was a "good Samaritan" even to a poor, innocent camel. I must admit, however, I was thankful that the poor camel did not know who had put the burning iodine on his back.

Who? The Anonymous Foundation Fund

It had been a long, hard day. I had finished my calls for the day, which was as much a matter of "fact" as it was a matter of "hope."

Sal's father had the largest cattle herd in all the Fringe country, more than 200 head of cows and calves. We had wormed all of them in the first half of the day, but it seemed as if it had lasted the whole day. Even though I did not consider myself a young man anymore, since celebrating my 58th birthday, it was a hard day's work for anyone of any age.

When I arrived back to the house, Anna told me that Boaz had come by and wanted to see me at my convenience. After lunch, I went over to see him, expecting to rest a little while talking to my dear friend.

"Hi Boaz," I greeted him. "How are you today?"

"Hello Dr. Bill. I'm glad you came to my store today."

"I think building this new store has given a tremendous lift to your business," I told him. "I see so many new workers here."

"Yes," Boaz confided. "My business has doubled many times. I now have twenty people making shoes and boots in the cobbler shop and there are four people working in the camel store."

"I see you have a new station wagon outside your store. Is that yours?" I asked.

"Yes it is," he answered. "I bought it for Rebekah to drive and she has already planned to get Miss Anna to go with her on a shopping trip to Addis Ababa."

"Anna would sure like that," I told Boaz. "They could make the trip in one day and have a few hours for shopping."

"I don't know how well we can trust this station wagon," Boaz said. "It was built in one of the Communist Satellite countries. I notice that our country is becoming more and more controlled by their line of government. It's probably too late now for Ethiopia to be turned around. One day, we'll just be another Communist Satellite country," he lamented.

"One good thing about our situation here in the Fringe country is we don't seem to fit into the Communist's plans for the future," I told him. "There just isn't enough wealth or profit potential here for them to care about us."

"There is something I would like to tell you about, Dr. Bill," Boaz said confidentially. "If you have time!"

"Please go ahead, Boaz. I have plenty of time."

"I know that for more than 35 years you have been in the Fringe country. You have often wondered about the hidden mystery, yet you have been very quiet about it, never probing for an answer."

I began to wonder what Boaz was talking about. *What in the world has been so secretive and what have I been wondering about all these many years?*

Boaz began. "You remember the story about my Father who lived in Lithuania for many years? He was not the only member of our Hebrew people who wandered about the earth. He had a brother who left the Good Samaritan Oasis at about the same time he did more than fifty years ago. When my Father started on his journey, Uncle Jonah and his wife also left. They traveled by camel caravan along the Red Sea

148

coast, through the Sudan and on to Cairo, Egypt. There, my Father and Uncle separated.

"Uncle Jonah and his wife crossed over the Suez land strip and went Northward toward Jerusalem and then, after a few years, turned South again. They planned to see Mecca, the religious capitol of Saudi Arabia. The endless waves of sand dunes that stretch across Saudi Arabia, and the intense heat at that time of the year made it impossible for my Uncle to continue. Their water supply was dangerously low and they wondered if they would be able to survive.

"He had a good knowledge of the camel, however, and realized that the camel knew the desert much better than he did. Both he and Aunt Martha knew they needed a miracle to survive. After loading his camel with the few remaining supplies, he and Aunt Martha climbed aboard.

"Not knowing which way to go, he turned the camel completely around two times, and then allowed the camel free halter, letting him go in any direction he chose. The big camel went to the top of the highest hill in the area. Then he turned himself around three times before heading in a distinct direction.

"My Uncle began to smile. Aunt Martha asked him why he was smiling and why the camel seemed to be so sure-footed while traveling in the new direction. Uncle Jonah told her that the camel is the keeper of the desert and he can smell water thirty miles away. The trusted camel took them to the safety of an oasis, which had a good watering hole. They survived what they thought was the end."

I sat engrossed in Boaz' story. His graphic language and gestures made every sentence come alive. I could tell it was going to be a long story, but I was enjoying my rest. Yet, I wondered what was the mystery that had stumped me for more than thirty-five years?

"The people at that oasis were good people and my folks learned to accept them as trusted friends," Boaz continued. "They stayed there at the Nafied Oasis for nearly a year while Uncle Jonah learned more and more about the area. Since most of the people around the oasis were farmers, my folks found a large area where no one was living and got a permit to farm their area. The permit gave them all rights to grazing, farming, and mineral deposits they might find on their farm, even though it was mostly desert land.

"Jonah was an honorable and intelligent man. He soon became a member of the local king's cabinet and the king used him as a mediator in nomadic tribal disputes in his district. In 1935, geologists from the United States discovered oil in his region of Saudi Arabia. Soon, the American Oil Company was formed and named the Arabian-American Oil Company (Aramco). This company has operated at full scale for many years and paid, millions, even billions of dollars in royalties to the Saudi government.

"The king honored the rights of those who had permits for their land. Uncle Jonah had usury rights to several thousand acres of desert land, which had become oil developing areas. He became a multi-millionare after collecting his royalties through the years.

"The 1960s brought unrest to the world and especially to the oil producing areas of the world. Jonah and Martha decided to take their fortune, while they could, and move to the United States. They could see that the entire oil industry in Saudi Arabia would someday become nationalized and believed that to protect what they had accumulated, they had better move quickly.

"Uncle Jonah and Aunt Martha were good people, very religious, and became good citizens of the United States. But, they never forgot their beginning in the Good Samaritan Oasis of the Fringe country. They gave many millions of dollars to a newly organized corporation they founded and named it the Fringe Country Anonymous Foundation.

"Dr. Bill," Boaz said. "Uncle Jonah is the one who started the foundation that supports your clinic and several other ministries here in the Fringe country."

I was amazed at this story! "Boaz, surely this is one of the greatest gifts a person could give to his kindred," I told him. I had wondered for nearly forty years about this Anonymous Foundation that pays our bills so promptly and so generously. I never once thought that such a close relative could be the "Good Samaritan" who provides so freely for the needs of the Fringe country.

Chapter Fourteen

Things Nearby
and Things Far Away

They All Pray

FOLKS WHO LIVE in the Fringe country are from diverse backgrounds. Most of them have different ancestries, are the offspring of those who emigrated from different countries many years before, and have numerous religions. But, one thing they have in common: they all pray!

Dr. Ling returned from making a country call. "Good for you, Ling. I am glad you are home. Boaz came this morning and invited me to come to Desert Gate One, where his kindred are leaving with a caravan of thirty eight camels for Egypt. I don't know what kind of ceremony takes place at high noon, but Boaz wants me to be present."

As I arrived, fifteen load camels were moving into place loaded with shoes and boots from Boaz' cobbler shop, along with fifteen camels with marquetry pictures from The Marquetry Company. Eight camels with riders would be meshed in between the load camels as needed. The caravan was complete. I stood alone, watching from the sideline.

The camel drivers greeted me warmly and then fell in line at the command of the Chief Driver. All men were dressed alike. They wore long blue robes and on their heads were turbans, with a long cloth which could be pulled over the nose and mouth to keep out the sand and dust.

The Chief Driver asked for the inspection of side arms. A slit trimmed in purple (the color of authority) in each robe on the right side of their waist allowed the driver to remove his hidden side arms quickly to be inspected for a full round of ammunition. Each driver was inspected and accounted for. The Chief Driver then said, "Fall out and inspect the load camels." They all walked in a group and inspected each camel's load from both sides of the caravan.

When completed, they all came to me and asked that I join them in a circle. The Chief asked Boaz to act as Chaplain. Boaz prayed for a safe journey across the Sahara desert for man and beast, and for safety for us at home while they were gone.

The caravan began to move to the north and progressed deep into the desert. The high noon desert air was bending the light rays causing the disappearing caravan to shimmer and shine in the hot desert. I thought about the camels laboring day after day in the hot, dry, lifeless desert. I stood alone, watching from Gate One until the caravan was completely out of sight.

Thirty days later, the caravan returned home. I saw Boaz at his camel store. He was more smiles than usual because the caravan's Egyptian trip was over. I said, "Boaz, why do you have such heavy emphasis on side arms when going on a caravan journey?"

"Dr. Bill," Boaz answered, "I knew someday I would have to address that question for you. "My people in the Good Samaritan Oasis have been breeding large camels for caravan use for two hundred years," he continued. "They carried no fire arms at all. But in 1944, they were caravaning from here to Egypt when a band of renegade nomads brutally killed seven members of our family, stole their camels and all the cargo of goods.

"The eighth member of our caravan was shot and left for dead. A good and lone traveler came by and loaded him on to his camel and took him to his home. He was treated and later recovered to tell this brutal story.

"My kindred had a meeting and made a covenant that this would never happen to one of us again. We would never travel unarmed and at the mercy of cruel people. All of us are trained in the use of side arms. On caravan journeys we all dress alike. All desert people know the purple slit on the right waist of the robe means a side arm is present. This may be a deterrent to crime for us because we have never had to use our fire arms in the past forty years."

Hesitating a moment, he then continued, "Dr. Bill, I'm glad you came to our high noon ceremony. Your standing with us in our prayer circle lets you know that you and Miss Anna will always be protected and treated with respect and kindness, even as all of our kindred, descendants from Abraham and Isaac, are treated to this day."

What Do You Love?

Our morning began early. We finished breakfast and were sitting on the porch. Boaz arrived with two work camels along with one of his hired hands. After greetings, Boaz began, "Dr. Bill, the Anonymous Foundation wants the land west of your house plowed and seeded in Sudan grass."

I said, "That's fine. What do they plan to make of it?"

Boaz answered, "That is not to be revealed at this time."

After hesitating a moment, he continued, "Dr. Bill, I know you have planned a furlough which will begin in a few days. I wish you would get me information about Death Valley Desert in California." I assured him getting this information would be my first priority.

Boaz left to begin his work and I began to digest our conversation. My thoughts were, Boaz is a desert man and often with pride speaks of the Sahara Desert in Africa as the largest desert in the world. He also has a folder of information about it. I suppose he has heard remotely of the Death Valley Desert in the United States. His love for deserts is astounding.

One week later we packed up and went to our home on Sand Mountain, Alabama.I spent the first month in veterinary practice with Dr. Mac on the highland rim of Tennessee. The last month we visited the western part of the United States.

Anna and I decided that Miss Bessie, my mother-in-law, would make the trip with us. We decided that two main attractions would be chosen for the trip. First, the choice of

Miss Bessie, and second, the information on the Death Valley Desert.

When we left home Miss Bessie said, "I have managed my farm for fifty years with twenty mules as the beasts of burden for all of our farm work. I want to go to Boron, California and see their twenty-mule team haul a load of borax from the mine to the refinery with just one driver in charge." Six days later, we saw the twenty-mule team with one lone driver and not a slip in the action. Miss Bessie said, "I see mules are still in charge of this industry, but before we leave I would like to tell you why I wanted to travel such a long distance to see these mules. I love mules and this love for them has been with me during my entire lifetime."

The next choice was Boaz' requested information about Death Valley Desert. It is ironic, but the twenty-mule team was hauling borax from deposits discovered in nearby Death Valley in 1873. As we approached the road entrance to the desert, we saw the gates were closed with a sign stating, "No day time travel allowed." Only night travel was acceptable. The officer in charge said, "Death Valley Desert is a deep trough with the lowest elevation in the Western Hemisphere. Often times in July the highest temperature of any desert in the world is recorded here — as high as 134° F.

I felt ashamed to return to the Fringe country with so little information. But Boaz is an understanding person and even this small report can be used in his collection.

In a few days our western tour was completed and we headed to Sand Mountain for our return to Africa the following day.

The next afternoon our British Jet arrived at Addis Ababa airport in Ethiopia. Sal was waiting to take us to our home in the Fringe country. Jet lag took its toll on Anna and I as we motored toward home.

Sal began our slothful conversation. "What kind of desert report do you have for Boaz?" he asked.

"Well," I said. "the report is not too long." I continued, "How is the grass project coming along?

Quickly Sal gave a pointed answer, "I'm going to let Boaz report on the grass field project." At this time my thoughts became more diligent. I wondered what happened to the grass field that needed Boaz' explanation.

We arrived at our house at exactly 5 p.m. I heard Sal say, "We are getting here on time." All our Fringe country friends were gathered around our house. Anna and I got out of the vehicle and went to the grass field. The grass was lush and a new net wire fence was around the entire field. Near the house was a new barn with an oval shaped hay loft above the regular first floor stables.

I asked, "What are you going to use this for?"

Sal answered, "Turn around and see for yourself."

Boaz and Rebekah were arriving mounted on a He and She camel. As Boaz and Rebekah stopped, each gave their camel the command to kneel for dismounting. Then they said in unison, "Dr. Bill and Anna, these are your He and She camels." I gave Anna the nod to make an acceptance speech. She said, "Thank you, we thank all of you. We love all the things you have given us but, most of all we love the camels."

Boaz said, "Dr. Bill, did you bring me a desert report from America?"

I removed a small folded sheet of paper from my pocket. Boaz read aloud as all the people listened:

Death Valley Desert in the United States: The smallest desert in the world. The hottest desert in the world.

Everything became hushed as Rebekah said in a muffled voice, "Is this all of the report?"

Boaz graciously declared, "This is a good small desert report, but our African Continent smiles because of the largest desert in the world." Boaz and his desert people stood quietly.

As I observed them, my thoughts continued: *To see this desert as a prize for their Continent. A prize of distinction, the Sahara Desert. A prise of destiny — a dry, starved and prostate desert. What do you Love?*

Rapid Blue Waters

Where does this little creek go? I asked myself that question many times as I enjoyed the little stream near our house.

But, if I were to enjoy Africa as I should, I must explore it and learn all I can about it.

The little creek near the clinic is really the main stream in this part of Ethiopia. It has beautiful, rapid, blue water, but to my knowledge, it is nameless. I have looked at every map I could find to see if it was identified. After a long search, I found that it is named the Blue Nile River.

This little creek flows Northward in our country, makes a turn into the interior of Ethiopia and then Northward again in the Sudan. From there it continues to Southern Egypt, on through that country to Cairo and empties into the Mediterranean Sea.

Boaz and I made plans to attend the annual African Animal Association, which was held for the first time, in Cairo, Egypt. We packed our bags and belongings into his large commercial station wagon and decided to take the route which follows the Blue Nile River. We were told that it was the best route, even though that was not saying much!

We followed the little creek until it became larger and larger with each mile. When we entered the Sudan, we noticed most of the people were farmers, depending on water from wells, shallow ponds and the river to help grow their crops. In the Sudan interior, the White Nile joins the Blue Nile and continues to flow Northward into the Nile River. The area between these two rivers is a region of one million acres where long staple Egyptian cotton is grown. Nearly thirty thousand families live in this area and produce two hundred million dollars worth of cotton each year. They provide the Sudan government nearly one-half of its income.

As I enjoyed the sights and sounds of this country, I noticed something that looked very familiar to me! The tall grass on our left reminded me of home in the U.S. It was the same kind of grass that is grown extensively near my boyhood home on Sand Mountain, Alabama. In the Sudan, as well as the U.S., it is an excellent feed for livestock. It grows in almost any type of soil and especially in semi-arid lands. The U.S. government introduced this grass into our country from the Sudan around 1910. Over the years it has developed into a very dependable tall grass and continues to be grown in all parts of Africa and the United States.

The highways improved as we went North toward the Egyptian border. Several areas had nomads living there in the scattered grazing areas. The number of camels increased as we reached the Northern Sahara Desert.

When we finally arrived at the Southern border of Egypt, I remembered reading about this miracle country of Arabic and Hebrew speaking people, where the Nile River flows into a large flat desert. The Nile overflows its banks every year, making the land fertile and supportive to many farms along its banks.

Further North, we noticed a population increase, particularly as we neared the capitol city of Cairo. Though still desert land, the Northern part of Egypt had many green oases dotted around the area. These oases were places where underground water works its way to the surface and vegetation grows freely. We noticed thousands of people living in these large oases. The largest oasis is El Fairyum, located fifty miles west of Cairo, with many more oases located in the nearby expanse.

"This is the one city I've always wanted our association to hold its convention," Boaz told me as we viewed the sights. "Cairo is the largest city in the continent of Africa and has many ancient pyramids, sphinx, and the valley of kings. My ancestry, Abraham and Sarah, lived near this place," he explained with tears forming in his eyes.

We were silent for a moment as we observed the many wonderful sights. Then I broke the silence by asking, "When we get to the convention, which animal do you suggest we support as the animal of the year?"

"I see the giraffe as the animal of the year," he replied.

We had already seen some advertising concerning the giraffe and had witnessed a parade of one hundred giraffes, each riding in a motorcade of trucks, with their heads raised high above the vehicles.

Boaz continued to give me a lesson about the giraffe. "The giraffe is a sleek and beautiful animal, which has continued to do its job for many centuries," he told me. "He should be rewarded this year for his fine job!"

I wondered what his job was. Without asking, I knew Boaz would continue to teach me.

"Let me tell you a story, Dr. Bill," Boaz began. "One time the zebra asked the Lord what He could give him for protection from the fierce lion. The zebra said, 'I have short legs and a fat body which the lion would like to have for supper. I have no horns, antlers, or a sting of poison to protect me,' the zebra added. Then the Lord said, 'I will give you the giraffe, with his long legs and neck, to eat leaves from the tops of the trees. You can eat the leaves from the bottoms of the trees. I will assign the giraffe to you, to watch for approaching lions.'

"You know, Dr. Bill, the giraffe has eyes which allow him to see in all directions without moving his head," Boaz continued. "Even to this day, you will always see the giraffe and zebra together. If the giraffe signals approaching danger, the zebra runs without stopping to ask about the problem. Of course, the giraffe has his strong legs and feet to stomp the enemy."

"That's a beautiful story, Boaz," I confessed. "I will help the giraffe to win the animal of the year award."

"If you will sit far to the right, wearing your safari hat, and holding my turban," Boaz said, "I will sit far to the left in the convention hall. When the voting is done, we shall see how the giraffe will fare."

At the convention, the time approached when nominations for the animal of the year would be made. We sat around in small groups, getting acquainted with new friends and talking to some delegates we had met before at previous conventions. Then, we heard the rap of the chairman's gavel, calling us to attention.

"This convention is open for nominations for the animal of the year," he declared. I noticed one member of the giraffe delegation, who had led the caravan we saw, was the first to rise to his feet.

"Mr. Chairman," he announced. "I would like to nominate the giraffe as the animal of the year."

Immediately, Boaz rose to his feet, waving his turban.

"I recognize the man to the far left, with the turban in his hand," the Chairman said.

"Mr. Chairman," Boaz said. "I second the nomination for the giraffe."

At this time, I stood and waved my safari hat. The chairman told the delegates that it was only fair to recognize someone to the far right of the convention hall.

"Mr. Chairman, I too would like to second the nomination for the giraffe," I said.

Then a familiar man stood, speaking with a pleasant voice which we all recognized. "Mr. Chairman," he began. "With an honest and pure heart, I move the nominations be closed and we approve the good and helpful giraffe as the animal of the year." We all stood with a vote of acclimation!

The assembly was adjourned. Boaz and I went to the outside exhibit area to watch the giraffe parade as they came by, one by one, holding their long necks down to receive the Blue Ribbons at the crest of their heads.

Then, they were loaded into their trucks, and left for their home in the regions deep in South Africa. Their proud heads extended high above the vehicles in which they were riding for their one thousand mile trip to the South.

Boaz and I returned home by the same route and noticed several things we had missed on our way to Cairo. Anna and Rebekah were waiting for us as we arrived at Barter Store I.

The next day I walked to the little creek by our house to look at the birthplace of the Great Nile. Some way I wished to tell the little stream what a great river it becomes, just by doing the same thing every moment of every day. I wanted to tell it how it crosses the largest desert in the world, the Sahara, and leaves along its banks fertile lands, before reaching the largest city of this continent. I wish my little stream knew that after traveling and blessing people for more than a thousand miles, it loses its identity as it empties into the great Mediterranean Sea, whose name literally means "the middle of the earth."

The Camel — Master of the Desert

Where was the original habitat of the camel? No one seems to know for sure, but legend says that the modern camel, as we know him today, may have appeared in the ice age, originating in North or South America. When the ice caps pushed down from the North, so it is speculated, he crossed the Bering Straits to Asia.

It is said that the camel had the instinct to feel the cold, wet air where he stood and counted the degrees of rising temperature as he traveled over the Bering Straits to Asia. He knew that his natural habitat was the desert and traveled thousands of miles to find it. Today, he is the master of the desert, as he has been for many thousands of years.

Around the Fringe country there are always many camel stories. While they are different, they always glorify the camel and always have a moral for the listener. One of Boaz' relatives told me an interesting story about a man who owned one horse, but needed to cross the desert to transact a business deal. He went to an auction to buy a camel to help him make the trip.

No one seemed to want a specific camel, which was marked with a tag around his neck, "ND." It was an old camel, but with a rather short desert crossing, he believed that his horse and the old camel could make all right. He bought the camel anyway.

The inexperienced desert traveler packed his food, water, and supplies, and with a compass and map in hand, he loaded the camel. He decided to ride his horse and tied the stone water jar securely to the saddle horn.

The little caravan was going well until the second day, when the horse became tired of traveling the slow pace of the camel. The impatient horse, which had been following the tracks of the camel, passed by the desert animal in a quickened pace. But, within a few hundred yards, it lost its balance and fell into the deep sand. In the process, the stone water jar was broken and the traveler's only source of water was lost. The lives of the traveler and his horse were in jeopardy.

The inexperienced traveler knew one rule of the desert: let your camel find water. This old camel led his master, horse and his supplies safely to an oasis within fifteen miles. The little caravan spent the night in the oasis.

The next morning, the old camel was dead. The inexperienced traveler had broken a law of the desert — he had taken an "ND" camel across the desert. He found out that "ND" was a brand honest traders put on their old camels, meaning "No Desert." That was why no one bought the old camel at the auction.

The traveler knew that his horse could not carry the heavy supplies and himself for the rest of the trip across the desert. Three days later, another larger caravan came to the oasis for water. After telling the leader of his plight, he was invited to join their caravan for the rest of the trip. Of course, you guessed it! Another camel led the way across the rest of the desert, taking the traveler and his horse safely to their destination.

After hearing this story many years ago, my love for the camel prompted me to believe that when one camel has carried his burden as far as he can, then another takes up that burden and completes the journey for him.

One day I made a veterinary call to a small farm on the edge of the desert. When I finished, I noticed some kind of caravan coming our way, but they were still deep in the desert. As they got closer, I noticed one driverless camel leading the way. Behind the lead camel were ten Jeep-type vehicles, with wide desert tires, following one another.

When the caravan got to the farm, they stopped near us. "Why do you have a slow moving camel in front of your caravan?" I asked the leader.

"We could not tell where the sand may be too deep for our Jeeps," the leader replied. "The camel's large, padded feet get the feel of firmness and we know that it is safe to follow him." Once again I thought, *The camel owns the desert!*

One day I saw a group of vehicles in the desert, all painted the same color and on the side panel were identified as "International Aeronautical Engineers." There were several camels with them and I wondered what kind of experiments they were conducting.

"I see your name on your vehicles," I said, "but what are you doing here in the desert?"

One of the officials told me, "We are traveling across the desert with these camels to test the reasons for their durability to fierce winds," he said. "The first 'wind tunnels' of all time were faced by the camel and he has always endured them for many thousands of years. In the future, you may see some of our airplanes with the durability of the camel!" he said jokingly.

It was the first time I had ever known that modern science could use the camel to test future airplanes. Since Anna loves the camel so much, if we could have an airplane that looked like a camel, maybe she wouldn't be so reluctant to fly!

161

Why Not an M.D.?

Often, when I'm introduced to a new person as Dr. Bill Isabell, they immediately ask about my occupation. When I tell them I am a veterinarian, some of them ask, "Why not an M.D.?"

It might take a long time to explain the answer, but I usually say that I really don't know why I became a veterinarian. I guess, it's just because I like animals. Some may say that my answer is a "cop-out." But, many people think I was foolish to follow veterinary medicine when I could well have been a medical doctor. Usually, they are insinuating that I could have made much more money as a medical doctor. And, they are probably right.

I don't intend to deprecate the medical doctor's profession or his ability to make money, because he does have the ability to help people in their physical and mental needs. He does his work well and we could never get along as well as we do without his help. But, let me show you how I feel about being a veterinarian, by telling you a couple of stories.

The first sound I hear in the morning at six o'clock is old "Sure Foot,' my Irish Setter dog. He taps on the door to let me know that he has retrieved my morning newspaper from the front walk. He's been doing this every morning since we became "modernized" a bit in the Fringe country. Several people around Barter Store I now get a daily paper from Addis Ababa. Well, Sure Foot wants his breakfast so I pat him on the head as thanks for bringing me the paper and give him his food. He is also my companion when I go bird hunting.

After I cared for Sure Foot, Anna prepared me a good breakfast of eggs, millet cakes (waffle style), and a large glass of milk. I always gave Anna a loving pat before I left for the clinic. That little routine pat always made my heart beat faster as I walked to work.

That particular day as I walked over to the clinic, I noticed a farmer plowing his field with a mule. I also noticed that Mr. Moab's mule was pulling the plow with difficulty. After examination, I found that the poor mule had a sore left shoulder. I treated the mule by placing a pad, which I had at the clinic, under his collar and he was greatly relieved. Mr.

Moab offered to pay me but I told him that I could use another bag of millet meal when I would return home from the clinic in the afternoon.

Arriving at the clinic, I learned that I was needed to treat a herd of sheep for both external and internal parasites. While treating them, I remembered that the sheep donated the wool for the coat I was wearing that cool day.

On the way home, I stopped to visit Boaz. He had a young camel he was training to replace the camel which I had to put to sleep because of its broken leg. Boaz told me that all camels begin their training at five years of age and are trained for twelve years. When they become seventeen, they are considered old enough to enter the desert.

When the day was nearly over, all my rounds, chores and plans completed, I went to see the progress of the new bluebirds who were building a nest in our new bird house. In my opinion the blue bird is the greatest of all songbirds in the world. They usually build their nests near houses or buildings, and they feed on beetles, caterpillars, grasshoppers, and other insects that are harmful to the human environment.

The bluebird deserves to be popular because they are beautiful as well as useful. They mate-off for life and the female sits on the clutch of eggs while the male brings her insects to eat. They do not allow other birds to infringe on their territory. If necessary, they lose their temper and chase off the other birds with distress cries and flogging actions.

I went to the house and Anna was waiting for me. It always made my day — just to see her standing at the door looking for my return.

At the end of each day, I made it a practice to define my day by writing in my ledger the day's activities. Then, I'd look over the entries and ask myself the question, "Did I pay my dues — as a veterinarian?

I'd remember my old dog, Sure Foot, who brought me the morning paper and I had given him a pat. Then I'd mark, "Paid."

I'd remember the millet waffles for breakfast and that the mule had been relieved of a sore shoulder while plowing the soil and Mr. Moab for giving me more millet meal. And I'd mark them, "Paid."

I'd remember the glass of milk and the cow I gave the special minerals to for her nutrition. "Paid."

I'd remember the young camel I had helped train for desert use, as though I had been responsible for it. I felt as if I were his godfather — even to all camels. "Paid."

I'd remember coming home to the new bluebird house I had built and hearing the birds sing, knowing full well that they would make great neighbors. "Paid."

All the day was finished and it was almost bedtime. I forgot to do one last thing — give old Sure Foot a "thank you" pat for doing such a good job of flushing the birds for me during an afternoon hunting trip. I went out on the back porch where Sure Foot stayed, and he was not there. I wondered where he could be! I looked down the back drive, but he was not there. I went to the front porch, even though it was not where he usually ends his day.

There he was at the edge of the front porch, waiting for the morning paper to arrive eight hours later. But, he was on the job ahead of time. I gave him the pat he deserved and that I owed. Then I went to bed knowing I would always be a veterinarian. To be sure, if Sure Foot ever needs his master or his veterinarian, I would be ready to answer, "Present!"

Who Are You? — The French Foreign Legion

Dr. Ling handed me a note to inform me that I was needed at the Sardo Oasis. This area is the furthest point we go in our practice — nearly seventy miles away. I traveled the well-marked road that led around the Fringe to the town of Sardo. Then, the last ten miles were out in the open desert before reaching the Sardo Oasis. Yet, the road is passable for a Jeep to travel most of the time.

When I arrived at the oasis, I was directed to a cow that was in heavy labor, with the calf in breech presentation. After removing my shirt and stripping to the waist, I washed and lubricated my hands and arms for the difficult calving.

The rump of the calf was protruding at the vulva. I had to push the rump back into its pre-birth position, then turn the rear limbs to point outward. The unborn calf was then pulled backward. It was very difficult and took about one hour before finishing. The calf would survive, and the owner was appreciative. After washing as best I could, I started my return trip.

As I traveled through the desert portion of my return trip, I noticed a large sand dune that had accumulated across the area, all within a few hours. It seemed impossible that so much sand could be moved by the wind in so little time. I stopped the Jeep to examine the depth of the sand while pacing several yards in each direction. I concluded there was no way I could drive through, around or over the huge dune.

One of the first desert rules I learned after coming to the Fringe country was never to leave a known path. Always stop and wait for help. If an inexperienced desert traveler leaves the known way, searching for his own way, he will be lost forever to the look-alike deserts, which often are larger than the whole United States.

I waited for five hours in the desert's quietness, when suddenly, a camel caravan of uniformed men approached me. The platoon of soldiers used their camels to find an alternate route and marked it carefully for future travelers.

Roads are seldom made in the sandy desert. They are just marked by experienced travelers from time to time, and changed when a sand storm may hide a previously traveled route. Many times, the shifting wind will move the same sand back to its original place, thereby uncovering the original route.

The platoon of military men did their job expertly before I had the chance to get acquainted with them.

"Who are you?" I asked the leader of the platoon.

"We are the French Foreign Legion," the lieutenant told me. "We were organized for desert duty to help people like yourself, who may be stranded in the desert."

I had read many stories as a young boy about the French Foreign Legion but I never expected to meet them. I was especially glad to see them that day.

The rest of the way home was without incident. Anna, as always, was waiting for me at the door, with Sure Foot wagging his tail as he stood alongside her. I soon forgot the awkwardness of a difficult day, because it had been conquered.

About the French Foreign Legion: It was created by the French Government in 1830 for service outside France. The

French formed the guard in the conquest of Algeria and French Somalia.

French Somalia has desert borders in common with the Fringe country desert in Ethiopia. The Foreign Legion units are still used as keepers of the deserts of Africa. They have freedom of the desert boundaries and aid people in their desert travels.

Old Mojo

Twenty years ago my camel study was given a new direction. Since there were no books or other available printed material about the camel, and simply because no studies or experiments had been done, I found a new source of information.

There is a close kinship between the cow and the camel. They are both ruminants, chew their cuds, eat large amounts of roughage, and their bone structures are basically the same. The major difference is size. A camel is nearly two times larger than a cow. Because of these similarities, I had almost memorized the textbook on cows for possible future camel needs.

Two years ago our Good Samaritan Oasis caravan company was on a caravan trip through the Sahara desert to northern Sudan. We were using old Mojo, a camel that was a little older and wiser than all of the other camels. His presence on any trip helped to control camels fighting among themselves and especially at night when we stopped for the nights rest.

One evening we stopped earlier than usual to spend the night at a desirable oasis. By nightfall, three other caravans had stopped along beside us. During the night various camels in the four caravans began fighting with each other by spitting cuds, biting, kicking or simply running over each other. When such fighting occurs at a lodging place, there are no pens or barns available to separate the camels from the various caravans.

The solution was to let each caravan group form its original unit and move out on the trail as quickly as possible. That night, this was done with cooperation of all the caravans that had stopped for the night.

166

Since the Good Samaritan group was first to take lodging, we were by desert rules the only one left for the entire night. The next morning while moving each camel in place we found that Old Mojo was gone. Our big gentle He camel had gotten into the wrong caravan line and had moved out some eight hours earlier with a foreign group due to an honest mistake by a camel driver. Our only choice was to continue the journey home without Old Mojo.

Sixty days later a small caravan of five camels brought Old Mojo home to Desert Gate I near Barter Store I. He had been shifted from one caravan to another in an effort to get him home using his cargo deck address as his proper home location.

I went immediately to examine Old Mojo as Boaz brought him to our camel barn. When Old Mojo entered the large stable he fell down in a sitting position in the center of the stable. He was not able to hold his head up.

My initial examination revealed a weak pulse, emaciated membranes, a loss of weight and his hump (his food pantry) on his back was swivelled and depleted. He had run out of water, out of proper blood volume, out of minerals, vitamins, sugar, protein and everything that was needed to strengthen him.

These symptoms caused me to open my textbook featuring cow diseases to the specific disease Down Cow Syndrome and at once I marked through the word cow and replaced it with the word camel — Down Camel Syndrome. The treatment and management in the book was followed completely and daily to save Old Mojo's life.

I knew about a new blood circulatory machine that through its ninety electrode body placements would greatly enhance his circulation.

Our American Anonymous Foundation, on the request of Boaz, had the $30,000.00 unit delivered for our use in twelve hours.

This treatment on Old Mojo was used around the clock, On the eighteenth day, Old Mojo stood up in the stable.

We removed the circulatory machine, but continued all other drugs and supplements.

On the twenty-eighth day, sometime before noon, Old Mojo moved out of the stable and into the center of our grass lot. Anna and I went out to watch Old Mojo graze. Then Boaz and Rebekah came and Sal and Ling brought their families. The pasture around Old Mojo was filled with our friends.

Boaz thanked all for coming to support Old Mojo in his recovery. Most people passed by to touch Old Mojo's hump, to see if his pantry of food was filling again. The usual answer was that the hump was about two-thirds filled.

Boaz called for attention again because it was high noon. It was his ritualistic time for Prayer (usually private), but because of Old Mojo, this time we were all included. His Prayer gave thanks for Old Mojo's recovery, and all that came and visited for the celebration and that divine care would keep all of us.

Anna was excited and overwhelmed because she kept count of the number who came. Her total was equal to the total of the inhabitants in our entire community — 292.

Old Mojo peeped up out of his thick eyelids, but continued to graze as all left for their various homes.

Chapter Fifteen

Difficult Stories

My Most Difficult Story

IT HAD BEEN a normal day of practice for me. The morning was used to treat a herd of sheep for parasites. Anna had gone to Rebekah's house to get some flower seeds for her garden's Spring planting. The warm Spring days were ideal for planting, to get an early start in her flower garden.

While Anna was still in the garden, I went to tell her that I had to go on a call that would take me out into the country. I planned to be gone about two hours and would be home for dinner.

When I got to the garden, I noticed that Anna was sick. She had lost her balance and had fallen to the ground. I yelled for Dr. Ling. When he saw that Anna was sick, he went immediately for some nearby neighbors, who helped me take her into the house. We laid her carefully on her bed, hoping it would comfort her, while Ling called Dr. Alex.

Dr. Ben Alex had been our medical doctor for more than twenty years. He came immediately to her bedside. I watched him as he examined her seemingly lifeless body. Then he told me that Anna had had a major cardiac arrest. Anna was dead!

Boaz read from the Scriptures and gave words of comfort as we laid my dear Anna to rest on a hill near Barter Store I.

Ten camels stood as honor guards on the hillside.

A Way Out of Adversity

It had been seven years since Anna had passed away. My whole world seemed empty with nothing but sorrow and questions. I knew no way out of my adversity. There were many problems but few answers. It seemed to become too demanding of me.

I recalled once when I was a young man, that when problems were too much for me, I hitchhiked on the highway to the ocean. I found an out for my adversity.

One day Boaz rode his camel for several days to speak for me in my adversity and I became a citizen of Ethiopia.

One time a little baseball team caused slight damage to their milk cow, but later made Old Sally a Blue Ribbon winner.

Once an old camel laid down his life and another camel came to carry his burden to safety.

It seemed that nature provides a way out of adversity!

One animal has horns, another has antlers, another a sting of poison. The goat climbs the ragged cliffs for safety. But what about man? Where is his way out of adversity?

Across those seven years, I had tried to make every animal do a better job of his assignment. The cow now gives more milk, the sheep grow thicker wool, and even my dog is a better friend.

One job remained. I had to let the world know the increasing plight of the Fringe people, who were devastated by drought and famine.

Yet, there was comfort and renewed strength, knowing that my Anna was safely waiting for me on the hill above Barter Store I. The Lord gave me eternal strength!

Plan One

The famine of the past few years had almost destroyed the spirit of all of us. We needed to find a way out of our misery.

One morning Boaz entered without knocking and with the quick step of a business man. "Hi, Dr. Bill" Boaz said.

"Hello," I responded.

Boaz continued, "I have a long story to tell you and you must listen closely. Rebekah and I have been trying to develop a plan to alleviate the famine in our country."

Boaz caught his breath and then continued, "Let me unfold plan one to you. At the present time, it is not possible to travel from here to Addis Ababa because of military control of all of the roads in our country. It would be best to go by camel caravan through the desert by way of Sudan and Egypt to the city of Cairo. Rebekah and I are wealthy from our successful camel store. Our money is safe in a bank away from our unstable Communist-like government. In Cairo, we will go to the bank that keeps our money, and I will give you one-half of all the money we have."

Boaz went on, "Pay your fare on a British jet to London and on to New York, and then to your kindred home on Sand Mountain in Alabama. This plan will deliver you from Africa to your homeland with wealth and freedom from hunger and with all the luxuries of America.

Silent for a moment, I then said, "Boaz, I'll stay right here with you." There was silence again, as I saw Boaz baffled, but studying my answer to his proposal.

Regaining his composure, Boaz said, "Dr. Bill, you are my brother." After another time of silence, Boaz finally resumed his business man's quick step and left saying, "I'll see you tomorrow when we all vote on our second and final plan."

I heard him walking rapidly as he went out of sight, but his rhythm was a little off due to my answer to plan one. I wondered what he had in mind for tomorrow, but today's proposal was completed.

A Called Meeting

The increased crop failures during the last few years began to take a severe toll on the people in the Fringe country. Boaz called a meeting of all residents around Barter Store I to decide on some very important issues.

171

"As we all know, the Good Samaritan Oasis community has supplied most of our food during the past few years," he began, "because of the severe drought. Some of the Fringe people to the South of us are already in large hunger camps. Unless the drought ends, we will all be forced to join them as hunger refugees."

The whole delegation did not like to hear what he was saying, but they knew every word was true. All the surpluses they had stored had been diminished long ago.

"The citizens of the Good Samaritan Oasis had a meeting yesterday and they have invited all of us to move to their community for the duration of the famine," Boaz continued. "They have hand-pump irrigation which has allowed them to continue to produce ample crops each year and they voted to share their community and opportunities with us."

Then Boaz asked the citizens to vote on moving to the oasis. "All in favor of moving to the Good Samaritan Oasis for the duration of the famine, please raise your hands."

The vote was unanimous with 291 people raising their hands! The citizens around the Barter Store I were about evenly divided between Hebrew ancestry and native African descent, but they were all agreed that moving was the best thing.

Boaz looked at me after the vote was counted. "Dr. Bill, I wish you would make a statement." he asked.

"I will be ready to go when the last caravan leaves," I told the audience.

One Thousand "Jobs" Are Here

During that week, most of the people had moved to the oasis. There were still a few of the leaders left who were staying to make sure that everything was in order before the final move. I felt that it was my duty, somehow, to let the peoples of the free world know about the famine in Ethiopia.

One day, I drove my Jeep to the South to visit the hunger camp where thousands of people were existing on starvation diets. I talked with one old man who seemed to need a comforting word. It was then I was reminded of Job, the man in the Bible who had been reduced to the lowest level of living. He sat in sackcloth and ashes, boils from his head to his feet, believing that God was punishing him.

These people were like Job, only there were thousands of them. They had lost their possessions and their families had been reduced through starvation and death. Some of them even thought the Lord was punishing them.

Their bodies were in a most weakened condition, but for some, their faith remained strong.

I was silent. I thought: There are a thousand Jobs here today!

While it was true that the drought had caused this terrible dilemma, the greatest cause had been the monarchy, with its leaning toward Communism. Most of the leaders did not even know how Communism works. The equal sharing of wealth, goods, labor, food, and even political power is what they preached. But, in this once Christian land, there was little hope that this sharing would become evident. The rulers were motivated by personal gain and had enacted laws much more severe than the Communists had taught them.

The draught was the straw that broke the whole system. A wall of secrecy had been erected to keep the peoples of the free world from knowing the plight of our nation. The army restricted travel by all people in the country and would not let the Fringe people go beyond a particular border.

Sure, they had given a sample of bread to the starving people while making them stay in their "hillside arrest." But, two hundred calories a day was not enough to keep the people alive. I wondered if the rulers actually hoped for the demise of the people, so they could have the land all to themselves!

I looked on them with compassion while fighting to keep back the tears. Then I prayed this simple prayer: *Lord, tell me what to do.* The Lord seemed to say, "Go down to the East side of the camp. A little ten-year-old boy will be waiting for you at a wellhead. I shall be with you!"

I stood by the little emaciated boy waiting by the well. Presently, a Westerner or an Englishman, I could not tell, approached me. "Do you speak English?" he asked.

"Yes, I do," I told him. "I am an American."

"Is this one of your little boys?" he asked. "How old is he? He looks so hungry."

"This little boy has been hungry all his life, for the past ten years," I told him.

The visitor was stunned when he heard the little fellow was ten years old. His skin and bones and stunted growth made him look half that age. Then the visitor lifted his head with determination and said, "I'm going for help!"

That man would carry the word to the whole world. Soon it would be in the headlines of every newspaper in the country and on the screen of every TV set. Help would finally be on its way. But for many, it would be too late.

I returned to my home, because I knew it was time to begin packing my things for moving. I was so thankful that the unknown Westerner believed as I did — that we are our brother's keeper!

The Most Difficult Day

The last caravan of camels had come to finish the move to the oasis. A battalion of French Foreign Legion had come to offer assistance. Everything had finally been loaded and Boaz told Sal to go to Dr. Bill's house to load his things.

When Sal arrived at Dr. Bill's house, he came running out to tell Boaz that the veterinarian was sick. Dr. Ben Alex was summoned and after examination, he told those who had gathered that Dr. Bill wad dead! He had died of natural causes during the night of waiting.

Again, Boaz read from the Scriptures and gave some words of comfort as Dr. Bill was laid to rest beside his beloved Anna, on the hillside near Barter Store I.

The French Foreign Legion Battalion of camels stood as honor guards!

The Benediction

Today, there is a stone monument on the hillside near Barter Store I, placed by the people of the community. They believe that the Lord looks down upon the place where Dr. Bill and Anna are resting.

As the Lord looks upon this now deserted hill, He seems to say, "It is good that you came to this Fringe country, Bill and Anna."

He also seems to remind the community, "That which I say is good for you, I will not take away from you."

Yes, the people near Barter Store I, in the Fringe country of Ethiopia, in Western Africa, will never forget Dr. and Mrs. William J. Isabell, nor will the memory of their dedication and love ever be forgotten.

On the stone monument at their grave sites are carved these words:

To Praise the Lord,
To remind each
that we are our brother's keeper.
Here Dr. Bill says,
Here I Raise My Ebenezer!
I Samuel 7:12

Epilogue

THEY WERE WRONG, of course! The Communists could not bring an end to the Fringe country people. The cry for help was heard in America, England and other free countries of the world. Volunteers, food and medicine were dispatched for their survival.

They were wrong indeed, if they thought Dr. Bill would be counted out. Even after his death, his life teachings live on in the people of Ethiopia.

Boaz is the chief shoe maker at the Good Samaritan Oasis and the rebuilding of his people is in progress. The camel is still the owner of the desert. During the famine, many of the younger ones were used for needed food. The older ones were turned out free into the desert. They will survive and once more be the friend of the desert traveler. They will live out their destiny in the dry, starved and prostrate desert.

Miss Bessie is in a Senior Citizen's Home in Alabama. She sold her Sand Mountain farm which is now cultivated by tractors and modern equipment. She is ninety-six years old, but still hopes to make it past the one century mark.

Enough! I will write no more.

Dr. Mac